The Com

Handbook of
Maths Terms

Prim
www.prim-ed.com

■ JACK BANA ■ LINDA MARSHALL ■ PAUL SWAN

The Complete Handbook of Maths Terms

Published by:
Prim-Ed Publishing
www.prim-ed.com

Copyright © Jack Bana, Linda Marshall, Paul Swan 2006

Distributed by:
Australasia
R.I.C. Publications®, PO Box 332, Greenwood 6924, Western Australia
www.ricgroup.com.au
United Kingdom and Republic of Ireland
Prim-Ed Publishing, Bosheen, New Ross, Co. Wexford, Ireland
www.prim-ed.com
Asia
R.I.C. Publications, 5th Floor, Gotanda Mikado Building
2-5-8 Hiratsuka, Shinagawa-Ku Tokyo, Japan 142-0051
www.ricpublications.com

ISBN 1 84654 035 6
PR–1069

Contents

Foreword

In language it is common for a parent, teacher or pupil to make use of a dictionary to check the spelling, meaning, pronunciation or origin of a word. In mathematics, however, where language can often prove to be a stumbling block, it is rare for a dictionary to be consulted.

In this publication we have tried to give brief and simple explanations of terms without sacrificing accuracy. When in doubt, we have erred on the side of clarity and simplicity. We tried to put ourselves in the place of the user and therefore kept explanations brief and tried to avoid words that would require further definition. To amplify the meanings we often included diagrams to illustrate the ideas. Where we felt that readers would benefit from an overview of key ideas about a particular topic, we included a detailed reference section in the latter half of the book.

We appreciate that when producing a book of this sort it is difficult to appease the purists while at the same time making it accessible to parents, teachers and pupils.

Abacus
A device with beads on wires as shown, used to perform calculations.

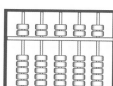

Absolute value [ ]
The numerical value of a number, ignoring the sign. [From the Latin *absoluere* 'to free from', hence to free from its sign.]

The absolute value of both ⁺7.5 and ⁻7.5 is 7.5.

Acre
A unit of area, equal to 4840 square yards or 4046.86 square metres.

Acute angle
An angle of size less than 90°. [Acute means sharp; see p. 86.]

Acute-angled triangle
A triangle where all three angles are acute; i.e. less than 90° [see p. 88].

AD
Abbreviation for the Latin *anno Domini* (year of our Lord) applied to years after the birth of Christ. [CE, for Common Era, is now often used.]

This book was first published in the year 2005 AD.

Addend
Any number to be added.

In the sentence 4 + 5 = 9, both 4 and 5 are addends.

Addition (+)
The operation of combining two or more addends to produce another number called a sum.

$$4 + 3 = 7$$

Addition property of zero
When zero is added to any number, the sum is that number [see p. 60].

$$7 + 0 = 7$$

Additive inverse (Opposite)
If the sum of two numbers is zero, then they are additive inverses or opposites of each other.

3 and ⁻3 are additive inverses or opposites because 3 + ⁻3 = 0.

List of mathematical terms

Adjacent angles
Angles in the same plane with a common side and common vertex.

e.g.

Angles ABC and CBD are adjacent angles.

Algebra
A generalised form of arithmetic where letters are used to represent numbers.

e.g.

In the sentence $3y + 2y = 20$, $y = 4$

Algorithm
A step-by-step method for calculating a result.

Alternate angles
Any pair of angles on the opposite side of a transversal that cuts two parallel lines [see p. 86].

e.g.

Altitude
Height or vertical distance.

e.g.

The helicopter was flying at an altitude of 300 metres.

am (a.m.)
Abbreviation for the Latin words *ante meridiem*, meaning before noon.

e.g.

10 am means 10 o'clock in the morning.

Analogue clock
A clock or watch on which the hours, minutes, and sometimes seconds are indicated by hands on a dial.

e.g.

Angle
Two rays with a common end point called a vertex, and the extent of rotation about a point [see p. 86].

e.g.

Annual (Annually)
Occurring once each year.

Annulus
Area enclosed between two concentric circles.

e.g.

Annulus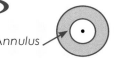

List of mathematical terms

Anticlockwise (Counterclockwise)
In the opposite direction to the movement of the hands of a clock.

Apex
The top vertex of an object or figure.

The top point of a pyramid.

Approximate (≈)
An approximate number or measure is based on an estimate.

- $78 \times 99 \approx 7700$
- The approximate length of this page is 24 cm.

Arc
Part of a circle, as shown [see p. 94].

Are
A metric unit of area equivalent to 100 m².

Area
The amount of surface.

The area of this page is about 400 square centimetres.

Arithmetic
The part of mathematics involving the study of numbers and their operations and properties.

Arithmetic mean
[See Mean]

Arithmetic progression (AP)
A sequence of numbers where the next term is generated by addition and/or subtraction with one or more of the previous terms.

e.g.

4, 8, 12, 16, ... and 20, 15, 11, 8, ... are both APs.

Array
An arrangement of objects into rows and columns.

The 12 stars shown are in an array of 3 rows and 4 columns.

List of mathematical terms

Arrowhead (Chevron, Dart, Delta)
A concave quadrilateral with two pairs
of congruent adjacent sides. [Can be
considered as a concave kite. See p. 93.]

e.g.

Arrow diagram
A diagram where arrows are used
to show the relationship between
members of two sets, as shown.

An arrow diagram may also be used to
solve problems involving combinations,
as shown. [See also Tree diagram and
p. 76.]

e.g.
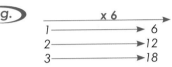

T-shirts
Jeans
Shoes

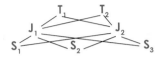

Ascending order
An ordered arrangement according
to number or size, beginning with the
smallest.

e.g.
6, 10, 14, 18 are in ascending
order.

Associative property of addition
When adding three or more numbers,
the grouping does not affect the sum
[see p. 60].

e.g.
$2 + (3 + 4) = (2 + 3) + 4$

Associative property of multiplication
When multiplying three or more numbers,
the order in which they are multiplied
does not affect the product [see p. 60].

e.g.
$3 \times (5 \times 6) = (3 \times 5) \times 6$

Asymmetry
Where an object or figure has
no reflection symmetry. [See also
Symmetry and p. 101.]

e.g.
The figures shown
are asymmetrical.

Attribute
A trait or characteristic.

e.g.
One attribute of a quadrilateral is
that it has four sides.

Attribute blocks
A set of plastic or wooden blocks
consisting of differing attributes of
shape, colour, size and thickness
such that no two blocks in the set are
the same. The blocks are used for
classification purposes.

e.g.

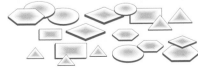

Average
[See Mean]

Axes

The plural of axis.

Axis

e.g.

A linear direction, usually vertically or horizontally; e.g. a bar or column chart/graph and a line graph each have both vertical and horizontal axes to represent quantities.

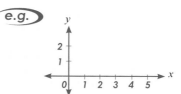

Axis of symmetry

[See Line of symmetry]

B

Balance

e.g.

Equipment using a pivoted beam to compare the masses of objects, or to weigh objects.

Bar chart (Bar graph)

e.g.

A diagram that uses horizontal or vertical bars to represent information as shown here; also called a 'Column chart/graph' if the bars are vertical [see p. 79].

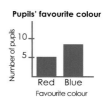

Base

e.g.

In the number 4^3 the base is 4 [see Exponent].

$6247 = (6 \times 10^3) + (2 \times 10^2) + (4 \times 10^1) + (7 \times 10^0)$.

In a place value system of numeration the base indicates the grouping; i.e. in the decimal system the base is 10.

The base of a 3-D object is the horizontal face it stands on.

In 2-D, the base is the horizontal line from which the height of the figure is determined.

base

base

Base ten blocks

e.g.

Wooden, plastic or foam materials, consisting of four different pieces called units, longs, flats and blocks, to represent place values in the decimal system of numeration.

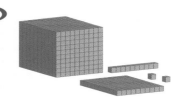

Basic number facts

The number facts needed to be able to carry out all calculations; i.e. the addition facts from 0 + 0 to 9 + 9 and the related subtraction facts, together with the multiplication facts from 0 x 0 to 9 x 9 and the related division facts [see pp. 58–59].

BC

Abbreviation for Before Christ and applied to dates. [BCE, for Before Common Era, is now often used.]

The Roman emperor Julius Caesar was born in the year 100 BC.

Beam balance

[See Balance]

Bearing

The direction of an object measured by its angle from the north in a clockwise direction by means of a compass.

Bicentenary

Two-hundredth anniversary.

1988 was the bicentenary of the first European settlement in Australia.

Billion

One thousand million; i.e. 1 000 000 000 or 10^9 [see p. 61].

Binary

Involving two possibilities such as yes/no, true/false, 0/1 etc.

Binary numbers

Numbers that are powers of two and usually referring to the base two numeration system which uses 0s and 1s and is the basis of all digital systems.

Binomial

In algebra, an expression consisting of two terms showing either a sum or a difference [from Latin and meaning 'two names'].

$$2b + c$$
$$x - y^2$$

Bisect

To halve, usually referring to an object or a figure; e.g. to bisect an angle, as in the diagram showing BE as the bisector of angle ABC.

Box and whisker plot (Boxplot)

A graphical summary of data that shows five aspects of the data: the lower and upper quartiles (hence inter-quartile range), the median, and the lowest and highest values [see p. 80].

Brackets (Parentheses)

That is ( ), { }, and [ ].

Breadth (Width)

The distance across.

e.g.

The breadth of this page is about 17 cm.

C

Calculate

Use a mathematical procedure to determine a number, quantity or expression.

Calculator

Usually meaning an electronic calculating device, which can range in power from basic to graphing to computer algebra system (CAS) capability.

e.g.

Calendar

A chart showing the days, weeks and months of the year [see p. 109].

Capacity

The amount a container can hold, usually related to liquids or gases [see p. 108].

e.g.

The capacity of the bottle is one litre.

Cardinal number (Whole number)

The answer to the question, 'How many?'. [0, 1, 2, 3, . . . is the set of whole numbers. See p. 71.]

Carroll diagram

A grid-like structure for categorising results. [Named after its inventor, Lewis Carroll—a pen-name for the logician Charles Dodgson. See p. 76.]

e.g.

The one shown can be used to classify a set of coloured blocks in a 2 x 2 system.

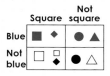

Cartesian coordinates
[See Coordinates]

Cartesian product
All the possible matchings of the members of one set with the members of another set, illustrating multiplication.

The 2 cups and the 3 saucers can be matched in 2 x 3 = 6 ways.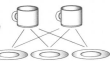

Celsius (C)
The scale on a thermometer where the freezing point of water is 0 degrees and the boiling point is 100 degrees. [Named after its 18th century inventor, Anders Celsius. See p. 108.]

Cent (c)
A currency or money unit of one-hundredth of a euro (€) or dollar ($).

Centimetre (cm)
A unit of length which is one-hundredth of a metre.

This page is about 24 cm high.

Centre
The middle—usually applying to a circle and then being the point equidistant from all points of the circle.

Century
One hundred, usually referring to 100 years.

This is the 21st century AD.

Chance (Probability)
The likelihood of an event occurring. [The numerical value of probability ranges from 0 to 1; and in the example it is 0.5.] The following vocabulary can also be used to describe chance: likely, unlikely, certain, uncertain, possible and impossible.

If you toss a coin you have the same chance of scoring a head as scoring a tail; i.e. the chance of scoring a head is $^1/_2$.

Chord
A line segment joining two points of a circle [see p. 94].

Line segment AB is a chord of the circle shown.

Circle
A circle is the set of all points in a plane that are the same distance from a centre point [see pp. 94–96].

Circle graph
[See Pie chart]

Circumference
The distance around a circle or the length of a circle; i.e. the perimeter of a circle [see p. 94].

Class boundary
The border between two class intervals.

The boundary between the intervals 31–35 and 36–40 is 35.5.

Class interval
A category of grouped data where the intervals are generally bounded by limits referred to as the class limits, but for some categories there are no limits; e.g. for the data listed here the 'Over 30' class interval does not have an upper limit.

class intervals

Age	Frequency
1–10	4
11–20	7
21–30	3
Over 30	2

Classification
Arrangement into groups according to particular attributes.

- *The set of whole numbers may be classified as odd or even.*
- *Attribute blocks may be classified by colour, shape, size and thickness.*

Clockwise
In the same direction as the movement of the hands of the clock.

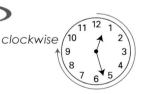

clockwise

Closed curve
A curve that has no end points. A simple closed curve does not intersect itself.

All three shown are simple closed curves.

Coefficient
The number of each variable in a mathematical expression.

In the expression $3x + 4y$, 3 is the coefficient of x and 4 is the coefficient of y.

List of mathematical terms

Co-interior angles

A pair of angles formed by the transversal of two parallel lines. They are supplementary (add to 180°); e.g. angles a & b, angles c & d, angles e & f, and angles g & h are all pairs of co-interior angles [see p. 86].

e.g.

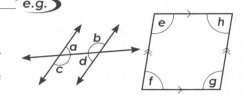

Collinear

Three or more points in the same line.

e.g.

Column

A vertical arrangement of objects; i.e. in an up-and-down layout.

Column chart (Column graph)

Also called a bar chart/graph, where results are represented by columns or bars, as in the example shown here [see p. 79].

e.g.

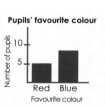

Combination

A grouping.

e.g.

In selecting two or more letters from a, b, c there are four possible combinations: ab, ac, bc, abc.

Common denominator

A name which can be used for several fractions.

e.g.

A common name for the fractions $\frac{1}{2}$ and $\frac{1}{3}$ is sixths, because $\frac{1}{2}$ and $\frac{1}{3}$ can be renamed as $\frac{3}{6}$ and $\frac{2}{6}$ respectively—thus 6 is a common denominator for halves and thirds, as are 12, 18, 24, 30, …

Common factor

A counting number which divides two or more counting numbers without a remainder is a common factor of those numbers.

e.g.

The factors of 6 are 1, 2, 3, 6 and the factors of 9 are 1, 3, 9; so 1 and 3 are common factors of 6 and 9.

Common fraction (Fraction)
e.g.

Any numeral (number name) for a rational number and having a numerator and denominator. [Fraction is from the Latin *fractus* 'to break'. Common fractions are sometimes called vulgar fractions.]

$$\tfrac{3}{4} \qquad \tfrac{5}{5} \qquad \tfrac{1}{6} \qquad \tfrac{9}{8}$$

Common multiple
e.g.

A counting number which is a multiple of two or more other numbers.

The multiples of 3 are 3, 6, 9, 12, ... and the multiples of 4 are 4, 8, 12, 16, ... so the common multiples of 3 and 4 are 12, 24, 36, 48, ...

Commutative property of addition
e.g.

Numbers may be added in any order without affecting the result (sum); [see p. 60].

$$7 + 3 = 3 + 7$$

Commutative property of multiplication
e.g.

Numbers may be multiplied in any order without affecting the result (product); [see p. 60].

$$5 \times 2 = 2 \times 5$$
$$3 \times 5 \times 7 = 7 \times 3 \times 5$$

Compass
e.g.

An instrument used for drawing circles.

An instrument for finding directions (has a magnetised needle that always points to the north).

Complementary addition
e.g.

Finding the missing addend [see p. 58].

What must be added to 7 to get 10? i.e. 7 + ? = 10

Complementary angles
e.g.

Two angles that together make a right angle; e.g. angles DEF and GEF are complementary.

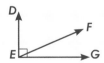

Composite number

Any counting number having more than two factors; i.e. 4, 6, 8, 9, 10, ...

Concave
e.g.

A concave shape is curved inwards like the inside of a bowl.

The upper part of these shapes is concave.

Concentric circles

Circles having the same centre [see p. 95].

Cone (Circular pyramid)

A pyramid with a circular base [see p. 98].

Congruent figures

Figures having exactly the same shape and size.

These two triangles are congruent.

Conic section

The figure resulting from a cone cut by a plane [see p. 105].

The conic section shown here is a circle.

Consecutive numbers

Numbers that follow each other in a sequence.

5, 6, 7, 8, 9 and 0.1, 0.2, 0.3, 0.4, 0.5 are both sets of consecutive numbers.

Constant

A fixed quantity.

In the expression $x - 8$, the constant is 8 and x is the variable.

Continuous data

Data not limited to integer values.

Convex

A convex shape is curved outwards like the surface of a ball.

Coordinates (Cartesian coordinates)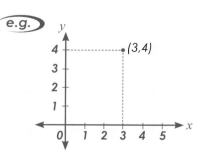

A pair of numbers or symbols that represent a position in a plane; e.g. the coordinates (3,4) are for a point that is 3 units to the right along the horizontal x-axis and 4 units vertically along the y-axis. [Cartesian is from the French mathematician René Descartes who developed the system.]

Coplanar

Being in the same plane; e.g. all points on the shaded left-hand end of the figure shown are coplanar.

e.g.

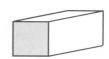

Corresponding angles

Angles in like positions in different objects or figures, particularly in similar or congruent figures; e.g. there are three pairs of corresponding angles in the triangles shown: angles A & X; B & Y; and C & Z; angles a & b are also corresponding angles [see p. 86].

e.g.

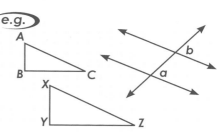

Corresponding sides

Sides in like positions in different objects or figures, particularly in similar or congruent figures; e.g. there are three pairs of corresponding sides (with matching marks) in the triangles shown: sides DE & LM; EF & MN; and DF & LN [see pp. 90–91].

e.g.

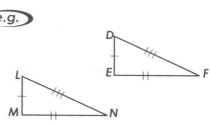

Counting numbers (Natural numbers)

The set of numbers used in counting; i.e. 1, 2, 3, 4, 5, ... [see p. 71].

Cross-section

The figure resulting from a solid cut by a plane; e.g. one possible cross-section of a cube is square as shown. [See Conic section and pp. 104–105.]

e.g.

Cube

A prism with six congruent square faces. [A cube is also a regular hexahedron; see p. 99.]

e.g.

Cubic centimetre (cm³)

A unit of volume occupied by the equivalent of a cube 1 cm x 1 cm x 1 cm in size.

e.g.

The pictured cube is approximately 1 cm³.

Cubic metre (m³)

A unit of volume occupied by the equivalent of a cube 1 m x 1 m x 1 m in size.

Cubic number

Any counting number obtained by multiplying a counting number by itself twice.

e.g.

4 x 4 x 4 = 64 = 4³, which is a cubic number.

Cubic root (Cube root)

The opposite of cubing a number (above).

 e.g.

The cubic root of 64 is 4 and is written as $\sqrt[3]{64} = 4$.

Cuboid

A box-like shape with all faces rectangular, but not a cube; thus also a rectangular prism [see p. 97].

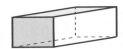 **e.g.**

Cumulative frequency

A 'running total' of frequencies, with the final cumulative frequency for a set of data being the sample total; i.e. 35 for the case shown [see p. 80].

e.g.

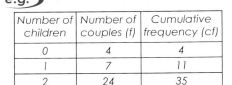

Number of children	Number of couples (f)	Cumulative frequency (cf)
0	4	4
1	7	11
2	24	35

Cumulative frequency graph (Ogive)

A line graph connecting the midpoints of the tops of the cumulative frequency bars. [Ogive refers to the shallow S-shape of such graphs. See p. 80.]

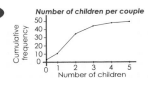 **e.g.**

Currency

A metal and/or paper medium of exchange that is in use in a particular country.

 e.g.

The currency in France is the euro.

Curve

An undefined term used in geometry to show the idea of a path that may proceed in any manner and direction.

 e.g.

Cylinder (Circular prism)

A special type of prism with circular ends [see p. 97].

 e.g.

D

Data

A term used to describe a collection of numbers or information. [Data is plural for datum, but data is now commonly used for both singular and plural cases.]

Day

A period of time – there are 24 hours in one day and seven days in one week [see p. 109].

List of mathematical terms

Decade

A 10-year period of time.

e.g.

This book was published in the first decade of the 21st century.

Decagon

A 10-sided polygon [see p. 87].

e.g.

Decahedron

A 10-faced polyhedron.

e.g.

Decimal

A decimal numeral that includes a decimal point.

e.g.

0.7   24.75   256.1   3.5

Decimal fraction

A decimal numeral for a non-whole number.

e.g.

0.4   0.25   0.316

Decimal place value system (Decimal notation)

Representation of numbers in base ten.

e.g.

483   75.6   74 290   0.396

Decimal point (.)

The symbol between the ones (units) and the tenths in a decimal numeral.

e.g.

In the numeral 3.5, the decimal point shows that there are 3 ones and 5 tenths.

Degree (°)

A unit of measure of an angle or of temperature.

e.g.

The size of the angle is 90°, or the temperature is 25 °C.

Denominator

In the fraction ³/₄ the denominator is 4 and indicates the fraction name—fourths or quarters. [From the Latin *nom* meaning 'name'.]

Density

The mass per unit volume of material.

e.g.

The density of water is set at 1 because 1 cm³ of water has a mass of 1 g, but the density of iron is 7.87 since 1 cm³ of iron has a mass of 7.87 g.

Dependent events

Where the result of one event depends on the result of another event. [See also Independent events.]

The probability of a lotto number less than 10 depends on what numbers have already been drawn.

Depth

Vertical distance downwards from a given position [see Altitude].

Descending order

An ordered arrangement according to number or size, beginning with the largest.

16, 13, 10, 7 are in descending order.

Diagonal

A line segment joining two vertices that are not next to each other; thus a rectangle has two diagonals but a triangle has none.

In the rectangle ABCD, the diagonals are the line segments AC and BD.

Diameter

The width of a circle, determined by the length of any chord that passes through the centre of the circle [see p. 94].

The diameter of the circle shown is the length of line segment AB.

Die (Dice)

A polyhedron, usually a cube, marked with dots or numerals on each face and used for games of chance. [Dice is plural for die, and is often incorrectly used for both singular and plural cases.]

Difference

The amount by which two numbers differ.

The difference between 6 and 10 is 4.

Digital clock

A clock or watch in which the hours, minutes, and sometimes seconds are indicated by digits rather than by hands on a dial.

Digits

The symbols used in a numeration system. [Digits are also fingers—from the Latin *digitus*—as fingers have always been used for counting.]

 e.g.

0, 1, 2, 3, 4, 5, 6, 7, 8, 9 are the digits used in our Hindu-Arabic decimal system.

Dilation

The increase or decrease in the size of a figure [see p. 103].

Dimension (1-D, 2-D, 3-D)

A property that can be measured in space where 1-D is linear, 2-D is planar, and 3-D is spatial, as illustrated by the figures here.

e.g.

1-D ——————

2-D ▢ 3-D

Direct proportion

Two quantities are in direct proportion when both increase or decrease at the same rate.

e.g.

Chocolate bars	Weight
1	40 g
2	80 g
3	120 g

Directed numbers

[See Integers]

Discount

The reduction in the marked price of an item [see p. 74].

 e.g.

Full Price	Discount	New Price	Saving
£50	20%	£40	£10
€100	40%	€60	€40

Discrete data

Information that can be recorded with whole numbers only.

 e.g.

The number of pupils in each class in the school.

Disjoint sets

Sets that have no common members.

 e.g.

The set of odd numbers and the set of even numbers are disjoint sets.

Displacement volume

The volume of liquid displaced by an object immersed in that liquid.

Distance

The length of a path—real or imagined—between two points or objects.

 e.g.

The distance across the road is say 10 m (along a line), while the distance from the South Pole to the Equator is about 10 000 km (around the Earth).

Distortion

A transformation which distorts the original figure [see p. 103].

e.g.

Distributive property of multiplication over addition
e.g.
Multiplication may be spread over addition [see p. 60].

$3 \times (4 + 5) = (3 \times 4) + (3 \times 5)$

Dividend
e.g.
The number being divided.

In the expression $35 \div 7$, the dividend is 35.

Divisible
e.g.
A whole number is divisible by a counting number when there is no remainder [see p. 69].

35 is divisible by 7.

Division (÷)
The operation of dividing one number (the dividend) by another number (the divisor) to obtain a third number (the quotient). [See the two items above and the item below.]

Divisor
e.g.
The number to be divided into another number.

In the expression $35 \div 7$, the divisor is 7.

Dodecagon
e.g.
A polygon with 12 sides [see p. 87].

Dodecahedron
e.g.
A polyhedron with 12 faces; e.g. the one shown is a regular dodecahedron [see p. 99].

Dot paper
e.g.
Paper printed with dots arranged in a set pattern.

Double
e.g.
Twice the number or amount.

Double 8 is 16.

Dozen
Another name for 12.

Edge

The intersection of two faces of a 3-D shape; e.g. the cuboid pictured here has 12 edges.

Element

e.g.

The member of a set.

There are 5 elements in the set of odd numbers less than 10; i.e. {1, 3, 5, 7, 9}.

Ellipse (Oval)

e.g.

A closed curve as shown, and one of the conic sections [see p. 105].

Empty number line

e.g.

A 'blank' line which may then be numbered according to the number problem being dealt with.

Empty set

e.g.

A set with no members. [Zero is the number of the empty set.]

The set of whole numbers greater than 1 and less than 2.

Enlargement

e.g.

An increase in the size of an object or figure while maintaining the same shape [see p. 103].

The letter O has been enlarged.

Equals (=)

e.g.

The symbol '=' between two mathematical expressions means 'is' and indicates that the two expressions name the same number or quantity.

6 + 4 = 3 + 7 may be read as 'six and four is three and seven'.

Equation

e.g.

A sentence stating that two expressions name the same number.

$$10 + 9 = 19$$
$$4 + 7 = 3 + 2 + 6$$
$$3y + 1 = 28$$

Equilateral triangle

e.g.

A triangle with all three sides congruent (of the same length). [All three angles will also be congruent, of size 60°. See p. 88.]

Equivalent

e.g.

Having the same value.

1 cm and 10 mm are equivalent lengths and $^1/_5$ and $^2/_{10}$ are equivalent fractions.

List of mathematical terms

Equivalent fractions
Fractions that are different names for the same number.

e.g.

$$\frac{2}{4} \qquad \frac{3}{6} \qquad \frac{4}{8}$$

are equivalent fractions as they all represent one half ($\frac{1}{2}$).

Estimate
An approximate calculation.

e.g.

32 x 47 is about 1500

Euler's law
For all polyhedra and for cones and cylinders V + F = E + 2, where V is the number of vertices, F is the number of faces, and E is the number of edges. [Named after the Swiss mathematician Leonhard Euler (1707–1783) who also invented topology. See p. 100.]

e.g.

Applying the rule to the square prism shown here 8 + 6 = 12 + 2.

Euro (€)
A currency or money unit used in most European countries. There are 100 cent (c) in one euro (€).

Even number
Any whole number divisible by two without remainder; i.e. 0, 2, 4, 6, 8, ...

Expanded notation
A numerical expression that shows the number represented by each digit.

e.g.

3475 = (3 x 1000) + (4 x 100) + (7 x 10) + (5 x 1)

Exponent (Index)
In the numeral 4^3 the exponent is 3. [See also pp. 72–73.]

Exponential growth
Applies to a quantity that grows at a rate proportional to its size; i.e. the larger the quantity gets, the faster it grows.

e.g.

3   9   81   243

Each successive amount here increases by a factor of three.

F

Face
Any two-dimensional (2-D) region, usually applying to a 3-D object; e.g. the cylinder shown here has 2 faces (top and base), while the square prism has 6 faces.

e.g.

Factor

Any counting number that divides another without any remainder is a factor of that number. [Factor is from Latin meaning 'to make', thus the word factory.]

 e.g.

1, 3, 5 and 15 are factors of 15 because 1 x 15 = 15 and 3 x 5 = 15; i.e. they all divide into 15 without a remainder.

Factorial (!)

A counting number multiplied by all the previous counting numbers.

 e.g. *5 factorial = 5!*
= 5 x 4 x 3 x 2 x 1
= 120

Factorise

Rename a number or algebraic expression as a product.

 e.g.

12 = 4 x 3 or 2 x 2 x 3, and 3y + 6 = 3(y + 2)

Factor tree

A diagrammatic strategy used to factorise (find all the prime factors of) a counting number by beginning with an equivalent product; e.g. two factor trees for 12 are shown [see p. 65].

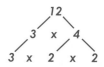

Fahrenheit

The scale on a thermometer where the freezing point of water is 32 degrees and the boiling point is 212 degrees.

Fibonacci sequence

The sequence 1, 1, 2, 3, 5, 8, 13, ... as discovered in nature by the Italian mathematician, Fibonacci—also known as Leonardo of Pisa—in the 13th century. [Add two adjacent terms to find the next one.]

Figure

Any 2-D drawing, or a number name using digits.

 *e.g.*

 37

Finite

Has boundaries or can be counted.

 e.g.

- *This page is finite.*
- *The set of counting numbers less than a million is finite.*

Flip

[See Reflection]

Foot

Imperial unit of length equivalent to about 30 cm. [The plural for foot is feet.]

List of mathematical terms

Formula

A mathematical rule usually expressed with symbols.

e.g. *The formula for finding the area (A) of a square region is $A = l^2$, where l is the length of each side of the square.*

Fortnight

Time duration of two weeks; i.e. based on fourteen nights.

Fraction

[See Common fraction]

Frequency

The number of times an event occurs; e.g. the frequency of boys and girls in the class is 14 and 16 respectively [see p. 77].

e.g.

Class genders

Boys	Girls
14	16

Frequency distribution

A table showing how often (how frequently) an event occurs [as in Frequency above].

Frequency polygon

A polygonal graph formed by joining the midpoints of the tops of the bars of a histogram, which are the midpoints of classes on a frequency table, with an extra class of zero frequency added at each end of the range to complete the graph [see p. 82].

e.g.

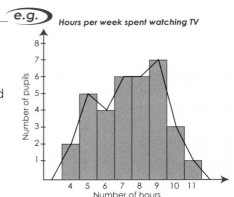

Hours per week spent watching TV

Function

A relationship which expresses one variable (the dependent variable) in terms of another (the independent variable).

e.g. *In the formula for the area (A) of a circle of radius r, $A = \pi r^2$, the area A is a function of r; i.e. the value of A depends on the value of r.*

G

Gallon

An Imperial unit of capacity that remains in common usage. One gallon is equivalent to 4.55 litres.

Geoboard
A board with nails or pegs arranged in a pattern and used to represent shapes with elastic bands.

Geometric progression (GP)
A sequence of numbers where the next term is generated by multiplication and/or division of one or more of the previous terms.

Both 1, 2, 4, 8, 16, ... and 5, 1, 0.2, 0.04, ... are GPs.

Geometry
The study of space and the shapes within it, in 1-D, 2-D and 3-D. [Geometry comes from the Greek *geo* for 'earth' and *metron* for 'measure' so the word means 'earth measure', which relates to its earliest uses.]

Googol
An invented name for very large number represented with a 1 followed by 100 zeros; i.e. 10^{100}.

Gradient (Slope)
Measure of the slope of a surface, a line or a curve in relation to the horizontal; e.g. the slope of path DA is $\frac{1}{2}$ because the 'rise' (CA) is half the 'run' (DC).

Gram (g)
The smallest unit of mass in common usage [1000 g = 1 kg].

The mass of a Smartie is about 1 g.

Graph (Chart)
A diagrammatic representation of numerical data [see Bar chart/graph, Box and whisker plot, Column chart/graph, Cumulative frequency graph, Frequency polygon, Histogram, Line graph, Pictogram, Pie chart, Scattergram, and Stem and leaf plot; and see pp. 76–85].

Greater than (>)
The relationship between two numbers or expressions showing which is greater.

4.1 > 4.09 $3x + 2 > 3x$

Greatest common factor (GCF)
The GCF of two or more counting numbers is the greatest counting number which is a factor of each.

The GCF of 18, 27 and 45 is 9 since 9 is the greatest number that is a factor of all three.

Grouped data

e.g.

Data that is organised into groups, according to size and usually of equal interval values; generally used for large amounts of data; e.g. the test scores for a large sample can be grouped as shown.

Score	Frequency
1–10	5
11–20	10
21–30	65
31–40	45
41–50	15

Hectare (ha)

A measure of area equivalent to that contained in a 100-metre square; i.e. 10 000 m².

Height

e.g.

Altitude or vertical distance.

The footballer's height was 185 cm.

Hemisphere

e.g.

Half a sphere [see p. 98].

Europe is situated in the Northern Hemisphere.

Heptagon (Septagon)

e.g.

A seven-sided polygon [see p. 87].

Hexagon

e.g.

A six-sided polygon [see p. 87].

The shape of a beehive cell is a regular hexagon.

Hexahedron

e.g.

A polyhedron with 6 faces. [See pp. 97 and 99. Note that *hexahedra* is one plural form, but *hexahedrons* is commonly used.]

A cube and a cuboid are both hexahedrons.

Highest common factor

[See Greatest common factor]

Hindu-Arabic numerals

Our system of numeration is a Hindu-Arabic decimal system [after its region of origin in the 9th century AD] and utilises the digits 0, 1, 2, 3, 4, 5, 6, 7, 8, 9.

Histogram

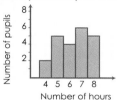

A chart that looks like a vertical bar chart but has no space between successive bars. The height of each bar or column represents frequency. The frequencies are shown on the vertical axis and classes on the horizontal axis. [See also Frequency polygon and p. 81.]

e.g.

Hours per week spent watching TV

Horizontal

Parallel to the horizon; at right angles to a plumb line [which is vertical].

Hour (h)

An interval of time of 60 minutes.

Hypotenuse

e.g.

The longest side of a right-angled triangle, which is opposite the right angle; e.g. in triangle XYZ the hypotenuse is the side XZ.

I

Icosahedron

e.g.

Any polyhedron with 20 faces. [One of the regular or Platonic solids is an icosahedron; see p. 99.]

Identity

e.g.

An equation that is true for all values of the variable(s) included.

$(x + 1)^2 = x^2 + 2x + 1$ is an identity, since it is true for all values of x.

Image

e.g.

The image of an object or figure is the shape that appears after applying a transformation; e.g. the triangle on the right of the mirror line M is the mirror image of the triangle on the left [see p. 102].

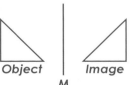

Object   *Image*

M

Improper fraction

e.g.

A fraction where the numerator is equal to, or greater than its denominator.

$^4/_4$ $^3/_2$ $^{10}/_3$

are improper fractions.

Inch (in.)

An Imperial unit of length that remains in common usage. One inch is approximately 2.5 cm.

Independent events

Where the result of any one event does not depend on the result of any other previous event. [See also Dependent events.]

When tossing a coin, each toss is independent as the result does not depend on the outcome of any other tosses.

Index

[See Exponent]

Inequality

A number sentence showing a relationship other than equality.

$7 > 3$, $3 < 7$, $3 \neq 7$ are inequalities.

Infinite (Infinity, ∞)

Never ending.

Counting 1, 2, 3, 4, … can go on without end; i.e. there is an infinite set of counting numbers.

Inscribed

When a shape is made to fit inside a second shape, the first shape is said to be inscribed in the second.

The circle is inscribed in the triangle.

Integers

The set of counting numbers, their opposites, and zero; i.e. … $^-2$, $^-1$, 0, 1, 2, … [see p. 71].

Intercept

The point at which a path crosses the horizontal x-axis or the vertical y-axis on a coordinate system; e.g. in the diagram shown, the intercepts of line segment AB are at $x = 2$ and at $y = 1$.

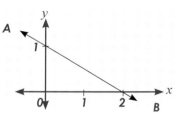

Interior angles

The angles inside a shape; e.g. the angles inside this polygon.

Intersection

The point at which two or more paths cross; e.g. X is the point of intersection of the two line segments shown [like the intersection of two streets].

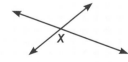

(cont.) The common elements of two or more sets; e.g. the two sets shown are the set of square numbers from 1 to 9 (Set A) and the set of even numbers from 1 to 9 (Set B). The intersection of Set A and Set B is the set of even square numbers from 1 to 9; i.e. {4}.

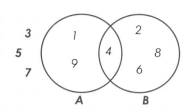

Interval

The amount of distance or time between two positions or events; or the range between two given numbers.

- An interval of 5 mm between two points on a ruler.
- An interval of 5 minutes between the start and finish of a race.

Inverse

The 'undoing' of a function or operation.

Multiplication is the inverse of division because it 'undoes' division, and vice versa.

Inverse operation

The inverse of an operation is an action that reverses or undoes what has taken place.

Division undoes multiplication and vice versa, as shown by 4 x 5 = 20 and 20 ÷ 5 = 4.

Inverse proportion

Two quantities are in inverse proportion when one quantity increases at the same rate as the other decreases, and vice versa; e.g. speed and the time taken over a given distance, such as 60 km, are inversely proportional as shown. [Note that the product of two such quantities is constant.]

Speed (km/h)	Time (hours)
60	1
30	2
20	3
15	4
12	5
10	6

Irrational number

A number that cannot be expressed as a fraction [see p. 71].

$\sqrt{2}$ π

Irregular polygon

A polygon where not all the sides are congruent and not all the angles are congruent; e.g. the quadrilateral shown here.

Isometric paper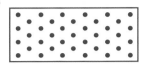

Paper with a pattern of line segments
or dots with constant lengths or intervals
[from the Greek *isos* for 'equal' and
metron for 'measure'].

Isosceles triangle

A triangle with exactly two congruent
sides, and therefore also two congruent
angles [from the Greek *isos* for 'equal'
and *skelos* for 'leg', thus 'equal-
legged'; see p. 88].

J

Joule (J)

A unit of energy or work, such that 1 J is the amount required to raise
1 g (1 mL) of water 1 °C. [Replaces the calorie unit and named after its
developer, James Joule.]

K

Kilo (k)

Prefix for one thousand in the SI or metric system.

Kilogram (kg)

A unit of mass equivalent to 1000 grams.

Kilojoule (kJ)

A unit of energy or work equivalent to 1000 Joules.

Kilolitre (kL)

A unit of capacity equivalent to 1000 litres.

Kilometre (km)

A unit of length equivalent to 1000 metres.

Kite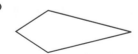

A symmetrical quadrilateral with two
shorter congruent sides and two longer
congruent sides [see p. 93].

Knot (kn)

A unit of speed of one nautical mile per hour, usually applied to wind or
boat speeds. [A nautical mile is approximately 1.85 km; see p. 111.]

Leap year

A year with 366 days and normally occurring every four years; i.e. 2008, 2012, 2016, ... are leap years (the extra day being February 29). [Note that century years must be divisible by 400 to be leap years, so that 2000 was a leap year but 2100 will not be a leap year; see p. 110.]

Length

The measure of a path or object in one dimension from end to end.

The length of this page from top to bottom is about 24 cm.

Less than (<)

The relationship between two numbers or expressions showing which is smaller, and therefore also which is greater.

4.09 < 4.1

3y < 3y + 1

Like terms

In an algebraic expression, the terms that are of the same variable and power. [Note that only like terms can be added or subtracted; e.g. by adding and subtracting like terms the example expression could be simplified to $2x^2 + 3x - y^2 + 4y + 1$.]

In the expression $3x^2 + 2x - 5 + y - y^2 + x - x^2 + 3y + 6$, there are five different sets of terms as follows: $3x^2$ and x^2 that are like terms; $2x$ and x that are like terms; $3y$ and y that are like terms; 5 and 6 that are like terms; and y^2.

Line

A one-dimensional straight path; e.g. the line EF shown here.

Linear equation

An equation whose graph is a line. [Note that in linear equations there are only one or two variables, usually represented by x and y, and the variables are raised to only the first power.]

y = 3

x + y = 5

are linear equations.

Line graph

A graph formed by line segments connecting points representing certain data, and with the horizontal axis usually indicating a measure of time; e.g. this graph shows temperature [see p. 82].

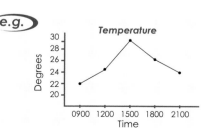

Line of symmetry (Axis of symmetry)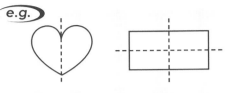

A line that bisects a 2-D shape so that each half is a mirror image of the other; e.g. the heart shape shown has 1 line of symmetry, while the rectangular region has 2 lines of symmetry [see p. 101].

Line segment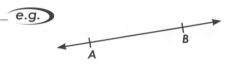

Part of a line that has two end points; e.g. line segment AB is the portion of the line from A to B.

Litre (L)

A measure of capacity for liquids and gases.

A litre of milk.

Loss

The amount by which the costs of a business transaction or operation exceed its revenue. Opposite of profit [see p. 75].

Lowest/Least common denominator (LCD)

The smallest number which can be used to name several fractions.

The common names for the fractions $^1/_2$ and $^1/_5$ are tenths, twentieths, thirtieths ... so the LCD for the two fractions is 10.

Lowest/Least common multiple (LCM)

The lowest counting number which is a multiple of two or more counting numbers.

The multiples of 4 and 6 are 12, 24, 36, 48, ... so 12 is the LCM of 4 and 6.

Magic square

The arrangement of numbers in a square grid so that the sums of every row, column and diagonal are the same; e.g. in the magic square shown here the sums are always 15.

4	9	2
3	5	7
8	1	6

Magnitude

The size of a quantity or number.

Mass

The amount of matter, commonly measured in grams, kilograms and tonnes.

Maximum

The highest number, or greatest size or amount.

The maximum weight of luggage per person on many aeroplanes is 20 kg.

Mean ($\bar{x}$, Average)

The mean or average of a set of numbers or scores is obtained by adding all the scores and dividing by the number of scores [see p. 78].

e.g.

The average of the four numbers 6, 7, 10, 13 is 9.

$6 + 7 + 10 + 13 = 36$
$36 \div 4 = 9$

Measure

A number assigned to a quantity to indicate its size compared to a chosen unit.

To find the size of a quantity or amount by comparison with a chosen unit.

e.g.

Choosing a centimetre unit, the width of this page is about 17 cm.

We usually measure angles with a protractor in degree units.

Measures of central tendency

[See Mean, Median, Mode and see p. 78.]

Median

The middle number of a set of ordered scores [see p. 78].

e.g.

In the set 8, 10, 12, 14, 16, 18, the median score is 13 since there are three scores both above and below 13 [just as the median strip on a roadway normally has the same width of road both to the left and to the right of it].

Mega (M)

Prefix for one million in the SI or metric system [see p. 107].

Megalitre (ML)

A unit of capacity that is a million litres.

Metre (m)

A base unit of length in SI from the metric system [from the Greek *metron* (measure) and originally defined as one forty-millionth the circumference of the Earth].

Metric system

The system of measurement units using the decimal system, and from which the SI units are derived [see pp. 107–108].

Midpoint

The point which divides a line segment into two equal parts; e.g. M is the midpoint of line segment AB.

e.g.

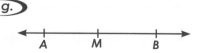

Mile

A unit of length in the Imperial system and approximately equivalent to 1.6 km.

Millennium

A period of a thousand years.

 We are now in the third millennium AD.

Milli (m)

Prefix for one-thousandth in the SI or metric system [see p. 107].

Milligram (mg)

A unit of mass that is one-thousandth of a gram.

Millilitre (mL)

A unit of capacity that is one-thousandth of a litre.

Millimetre (mm)

A unit of length that is one-thousandth of a metre.

Million

A thousand thousand; i.e. 1 000 000 or 10^6 [see p. 61].

Millisecond

One thousandth of a second of time.

Minimum

The smallest number, size, or amount.

 The minimum temperature in the city last night was 1 °C.

Minus (−)

Subtract or take away.

 Ten minus three is seven; i.e. $10 - 3 = 7$.

The symbol used to show a negative amount; [sometimes read as 'minus two', but should be read as 'negative two'].

$$^-2$$

Minute

One-sixtieth of both a unit of time of one hour, and a unit of angle measure of one degree [originating from the ancient Babylonians who used a base of 60 to represent numbers; see p. 109 and p. 111].

Mixed numeral

A number name consisting of both a base ten numeral and a fraction.

$15^3/_4$ and $37^1/_2$ are mixed numerals.

Mode

The most common score in a set of data. [Mode is from the Latin *modus*, and the French *mode* meaning 'fashion', so it is the most fashionable score. See p. 78.]

e.g.

In the set of scores 6, 6, 7, 8, 8, 8, 9, 10, 10, the mode is 8.

Month

A period of time—a year is divided into 12 months [see pp. 109–110].

Multi-base Arithmetic Blocks (MAB)

Wooden, plastic or foam blocks to represent numbers in a variety of bases [see Base ten blocks].

Multiple

A multiple of a given counting number is any number into which it will divide without remainder.

e.g.

The multiples of 3 are 0, 3, 6, 9, 12, ...

Multiplication (x)

Repeated addition, calculated by operating on two numbers to find their product. [See also Cartesian product and Array.]

e.g.

$$3 + 3 + 3 + 3 = 4 \times 3 = 12$$

Multiplication property of one

The product of any number and one is that number [see p. 60].

e.g.

$$16 \times 1 = 16$$

Multiplication property of zero

The product of any number and zero is zero [see p. 60].

e.g.

$$16 \times 0 = 0$$

Multiplier

A number multiplying another number.

e.g.

When 9 is multiplied by 4, the multiplier is 4.

N

Natural number

[See Counting numbers]

Nautical mile

A unit of length around the Earth's surface determined by the arc of an angle of one minute (one-sixtieth of a degree) at the Earth's centre, and used in navigation [1 nautical mile ≈ 1.85 km; see p. 111].

List of mathematical terms

Negative number
A real number less than zero, and an opposite to a positive real number.

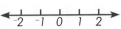
-2 is the opposite to 2 and vice versa.

Net
A flat 2-D pattern which can be folded to make a model of a 3-D object; e.g. the net to the right can be folded to make a cube.

Network
A system of curves and/or line segments with intersections (nodes) drawn to represent paths or routes and their intersections.

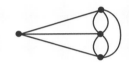

Node (Junction)
A point of intersection in a network of paths [see Network].

Nonagon
A nine-sided polygon [see p. 87].

Not equal (≠)
Two numbers or quantities that are not the same are said to be not equal.

$$6 + 5 \neq 10$$
$$2\ cm \neq 21\ mm$$

Number line
A line where all points have a numerical value. [Once any two points are numbered, such as 0 and 1 here, then all other points on the line automatically correspond to a number.]

Number pattern
An organised arrangement or sequence of numbers.

$$0,\ 5,\ 10,\ 15,\ 20,\ ...$$

Number sentence
An equality or inequality concerning numbers.

$12 \div 5 = 2.4$ and $16 > 5 \times 3$ are both number sentences.

Numeral (Number name)
One or more symbols to represent a number. [From the Latin *enumerate* meaning 'to count out'; see pp. 61–62.]

XV and 15 are two numerals which represent the number fifteen.

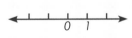

Numerator

The number above the fraction line (vinculum) which tells how many of the named fraction are being considered.

 In the fraction $^3/_5$ the numerator is 3, indicating that there are 3 fifths.

Object

A physical thing which is real and therefore 3-D [as opposed to a figure which is a drawing and therefore 2-D].

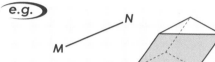 *The figure here is a 2-D drawing of a 3-D object that is a cup.*

Oblique

Slanting; i.e. any shape that is neither vertical nor horizontal is in an oblique position; e.g. the line segment MN and the 3-D object are oblique on this page.

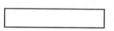

Oblong

A rectangle that is not square [see p. 93].

Obtuse angle

An angle of size greater than 90° and less than 180°. [Obtuse means blunt; see p. 86.]

 Angle EFG is an obtuse angle.

Obtuse-angled triangle

A triangle with one obtuse (blunt) angle [see p. 88].

Octagon

An eight-sided polygon [see p. 87].

Octahedron

A polyhedron with eight faces [see p. 99].

Odd number

A whole number not divisible by two; i.e. 1, 3, 5, 7, 9, ...

Odds

The ratio of the probability of an event not occurring to the probability that it will occur, or vice versa.

 *When tossing two coins the odds against a result of two heads is 3:1; i.e. three chances against (HT, TH, TT) and one chance for a pair of heads (HH).*

[The odds for two heads is thus 1:3, but odds are usually stated against an event occurring.]

One-dimensional (Linear) (1-D)
A path or line having only length.

e.g.
Both figures shown
here are 1-D.

One-to-one correspondence
A pairing of the members of one set
with the members of another set so
that there are none unmatched;
e.g. the set of cups is in one-to-one
correspondence with the set of
saucers.

e.g.

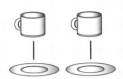

Open curve
Any 2-D figure that has end points [see
also Closed curve].

e.g.

Open sentence
A mathematical sentence containing
one or more pro-numerals.

e.g.
$6 + y = 10$; $z \times z = 25$; $10 - w = 9$
are open sentences.

Operations with numbers
Using two or more numbers to
create another number. There are six
possibilities as shown.

e.g.

Addition	$3 + 5 = 8$
Subtraction	$8 - 5 = 3$
Multiplication	$2 \times 4 = 8$
Division	$8 \div 4 = 2$
Exponent	$2^3 = 8$
Root	$\sqrt[3]{8} = 2$

Opposites
-2 and 2 are opposites because they
are equidistant from zero and therefore
their sum is zero. [Zero is its own
opposite.]

e.g.

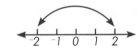

Order of operations
The conventional order in which
operations must be performed in
a numerical expression, and given
by the pneumonic B | I | MD | AS,
where B = Brackets to be worked first,
I = Indices next, then M = Multiplication
and D = Division together left-to-right as
they occur, and finally A = Addition and
S = Subtraction together left-to-right as
they occur.

e.g.
See the steps in the following
expression:

$20 \div 5 \times 6 + (16 - 3) - 3 \times 2^3 + 9$ **[B]**

$= 20 \div 5 \times 6 + 13 - 3 \times 2^3 + 9$ **[I]**

$= 20 \div 5 \times 6 + 13 - 3 \times 8 + 9$ **[MD]**

$= 24 + 13 - 24 + 9$ **[AS]**

$= 22$

Order of rotational symmetry
The number of times a figure appears to retain its original orientation during one
complete rotation about a fixed point. [See Rotational symmetry and p. 101.]

Ordered pair

A pair of objects or numbers where the order is significant; e.g. a position in a plane can be identified by an ordered pair of numbers such as (4,3) which indicate a point 4 units horizontally to the right from the origin and 3 units vertically. [Note that (4,3) and (3,4) are thus different positions.]

e.g.

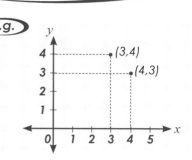

Ordering (Seriating)

Placing in order according to an attribute such as size or numerical value.

e.g.

21   18   15   12   9

The numbers shown here are in descending order from left to right.

Ordinal number

A number used to indicate the position of an object in an ordered sequence.

e.g.

1st, 2nd, 3rd, 4th etc.

Origin

The point of intersection of the two or three coordinate axes, and its Cartesian coordinates will be (0, 0) in 2-D or (0, 0, 0) in 3-D.

Ounce

An Imperial unit of weight that remains in common usage. One ounce is approximately 28 grams.

Outlier

A data item that is much lower or much higher than the main body of data; [lies outside the main set of data].

e.g.

In the set of scores 2, 11, 11, 12, 12, 13, 14, 14, 14, 15, the score of 2 is an outlier.

Oval

[See Ellipse]

Ovoid

Egg-shaped object or figure. [From ovum meaning egg or ova (plural).]

e.g.

P

Palindrome

A number name, date, word, or sentence that reads the same both forwards and backwards.

e.g.

747
level

01–02–2010
Madam I'm Adam

Parabola

The conic section obtained by cutting a cone from its curved surface, parallel to its slope and through its base. [Note that a parabola is symmetrical about its vertex as pictured; see p. 105.]

The cross-section of a headlight reflector, as shown.

Parallel lines

Lines in the same plane with no common points, so they are always the same distance apart [see p. 86].

Parallelogram

A quadrilateral with both pairs of opposite sides parallel, and therefore its opposite sides are congruent [see p. 92].

Partition

Dividing or 'breaking up'.

128 could be partitioned as 100 + 20 + 8, or as 32 + 32 + 32 + 32, etc.

Pascal's triangle

The binomial coefficients, also used to calculate probabilities of binary events, and which are arranged in a triangle as shown, with the triangle easily extended by following the pattern. [Blaise Pascal was a famous French mathematician who lived in the 17th century and the unit of pressure is named after him.]

```
          1   1
        1   2   1
      1   3   3   1
    1   4   6   4   1
  1   5  10  10   5   1
1   6  15  20  15   6   1
```

NB: 1 is not placed at the top of the triangle as it was not part of Pascal's triangle.

Pattern

A repeated design or arrangement of numbers, letters, shapes, colours etc.

1, 2, 3, 1, 2, 3, 1, 2, 3, 1, 2, 3

■ ● ▲ ● ▲ ■ ● ▲ ● ▲

Pattern blocks

Sets of plastic, wood or foam shapes in the form of triangles, rhombuses, squares, trapeziums and hexagons.

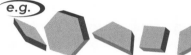

Pegboard

A plastic or wooden board containing a set pattern of holes into which pegs can be placed.

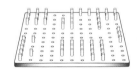

Pence

A currency or money unit equal to one-hundredth of a pound (£).

Pentagon

A five-sided polygon [see p. 87].

Pentomino

[See Polyomino]

Percent/Percentage (%)

Hundredths. [The symbol % originates from the name 100.]

7 percent is 7 hundredths;
15% = $^{15}/_{100}$

Perfect number

A counting number which is the sum of all its factors except itself.

6 is a perfect number because the factors of 6 are 1, 2, 3, and 6, and 1 + 2 + 3 = 6.

Perimeter

The length of the boundary of a plane region. [From the Greek *peri* meaning 'around' and *metron* meaning 'measure'.]

The distance around the edges of this page.

Permutation

The ordered arrangement of a set of objects or symbols.

There are six possible permutations for the three letters A, B, C; i.e. ABC, ACB, BAC, CAB, BCA, CBA.

Perpendicular

At right angles. [From the Latin *perpendiculum*, for a hanging plumb line.]

The two lines shown are perpendicular to each other.

Pi (π)

The Greek letter used in mathematics to indicate the ratio of the circumference to the diameter of any circle; i.e. $\pi \approx 3.1416$.

Pictogram (Pictograph; Picture graph)

A graph that represents data in picture form, and where one picture may represent one or more units [see p. 83].

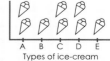

Ice-creams sold at the canteen on Monday

A   B   C   D   E
Types of ice-cream

List of mathematical terms

Pie chart (Pie graph; Circle graph)

A graph in which the sectors of a circle are used to show a whole in terms of its parts; i.e. each sector represents a category and its fraction of the total [see p. 83].

Ways of getting to school

Pint

An Imperial unit of capacity that remains in common usage. One pint is approximately 570 ml.

Place value

The value of each place in a numeration system. [Thus the value of a digit depends on its position in a numeral.]

In the numeral 643.5, the place values in order from the left are hundreds, tens, ones and tenths.

Plane

In geometry, a surface that is flat and has no boundaries.

Plane of symmetry

The plane that cuts a 3-D object in half, such that each half is a mirror image of the other with the plane as the mirror [see p. 101].

Platonic solids (Regular solids)

The five polyhedra in which all faces are congruent and all angles are congruent; i.e. the regular tetrahedron, hexahedron (cube), octahedron, dodecahedron and icosahedron. [Named after Plato the philosopher and mathematician in ancient Greece who stated that they represented the five elements of earth, wind, fire, water and the heavens or universe; see p. 99.]

Plumb line

A vertical line. [From the Latin *plumbum* meaning 'lead' and based on the use of a piece of lead on a cord to check vertical positioning. See also Perpendicular.]

Plus (Add , +)

The expression 9 + 5 may be read as 'nine and five', as 'nine add five' or as 'nine plus five'.

pm (p.m.)

Abbreviation for the Latin words *post meridiem* meaning after noon.

6 pm means 6 o'clock in the evening.

Point

An undefined term in geometry that indicates a position in space.

Polygon

Any simple closed curve consisting of line segments. [From the Greek *polus* meaning 'many' and *gonia* meaning 'angle'; see p. 87.]

e.g. a triangle and a quadrilateral are polygons.

Polyhedra (Polyhedrons)

Plural for polyhedron [see below].

Polyhedron

A three-dimensional shape consisting of plane faces. [From the Greek *polus* meaning 'many' and *hedra* meaning 'base'; see p. 97.]

Polynomial

In algebra, an expression including two or more terms, where each term consists of a coefficient and a variable raised to the power of zero or any positive integer. [See also Binomial.]

e.g.
$$x^2 + 3x + 2$$
$$5y + 7$$
$$6z^3 + z - 4$$
are polynomials.

Polyomino

A plane shape of congruent squares, where each square is connected to at least one of the others by a common side, and the number of squares determines the name; with one example of four types shown here.

e.g. Domino
Triomino
Tetromino
Pentomino

Population

All the members of any group being considered.

e.g.
• All the girls in the school.
• All the counting numbers.

Positive number

A real number more than zero, and an opposite to a negative real number.

e.g.

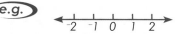

-2 is the opposite to 2 and vice versa.

Pound

An Imperial unit of weight that remains in common usage. One pound is approximately 0.45 kg.

Pound (£)

A currency or money unit. There are 100 pence (p) in one pound (£).

Power

When a number is expressed with an exponent (index), the index indicates the power of the base number.

e.g. 4^3 is the third power of 4, and 32 is the fifth power of 2 because $32 = 2^5$

Prime factor

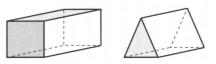

A prime number that will divide into a given counting number without remainder [see p. 65].

2, 5, and 7 are the prime factors of 70.

Prime number

A counting number with exactly two factors; i.e. 2, 3, 5, 7, 11, 13, ... [Note that 1 is not a prime as it has only one factor and, like zero, is considered a special number.]

Prism

A three-dimensional shape with parallel and congruent end faces, with the shape of the pair of congruent faces naming the prism; e.g. the first figure shows both a square prism and a rectangular prism, while the other is a triangular prism [see p. 97].

Probability

[See Chance]

Product

The result of multiplying two or more numbers together.

The product of 4 and 5 is 20; i.e. 4 x 5 = 20.

Profit

The amount by which the revenue exceeds the costs of a business transaction or operation. Opposite of loss [see p. 75].

Pro-numeral

e.g.

A symbol for a numeral in an expression or equation.

In the number sentence $2y + 3 = 13$, y is a pro-numeral for 5.

Proper fraction

e.g.

Any fraction representing a number less than one.

$^1/_4$ $^3/_8$ $^7/_{10}$

Proportion

e.g.

A mathematical sentence which states that two ratios are equal.

2:5 = 4:10 (read as 'two is to five as four is to ten') and $^3/_4 = ^9/_{12}$ are proportions.

Protractor

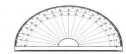

An instrument for measuring angles; semicircular or circular and graduated in degrees around its circumference.

Pyramid

A polyhedron with a polygonal base and the other faces triangles with a common vertex also called the apex. [Note that a cone is a special type of pyramid. See p. 98.]

Pythagoras

The Greek mathematician who lived in the 6th century BC and whose name is given to the famous rule about right-angled triangles; i.e. that the square on the hypotenuse is the sum of the squares on the other two sides; e.g. in the triangle shown, $3^2 + 4^2 = 5^2$.

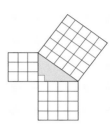

Pythagorean triples

Integral triples that are the dimensions of right-angled triangles, and thus satisfy the rule of Pythagoras. Some of the common ones are shown here.

3, 4, 5 and their multiples of 6, 8, 10 etc.
5, 12, 13 and their multiples 10, 24, 26 etc.
7, 24, 25 and their multiples of 14, 48, 50 etc.

Quadrant

A quarter of a circular region; e.g. the north-east quarter as shown here.

A quadrant is also one of the four sectors of a coordinate plane determined by the x-y axes, and where the quadrants by convention are numbered in the order shown here.

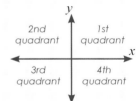

Quadratic equation

An equation of the form $ax^2 + bx + c = 0$, where $a \neq 0$

$3x^2 - 1 = 0$ $x^2 + 4x = 0$
$x^2 + 5x + 6 = 0$

Quadrilateral

Any polygon that has four sides [from the Latin *quadri* meaning 'four' and *latus* meaning 'side'; see pp. 92–93].

Quartile

When data is arranged in order of size from the least to the greatest, each 25 percent of the frequencies is called a quartile.

The top quartile of the pupils who sat a test is the set of pupils who scored the top 25% of the results.

List of mathematical terms

Quotient

The result of a division. [From the Latin *quotiens* meaning 'how many times'.]

e.g. When 24 is divided by 8, the quotient is 3.

R

Radian

The size of an angle at the centre of a circle formed by two radii and an arc that is the length of the radius. [Note that 1 radian ≈ 57°.]

e.g.

Radius

A line segment with one end point as the centre of a circle and the other end point on the circle. [The plural is radii or radiuses. See p. 94].

e.g.

Random sample

A sample chosen from a population in such a way that all members have an equal chance of being selected.

Range

In statistics, the difference between the greatest and least values in a set of data.

e.g. In a set of scores where the lowest is 40 and the highest is 90, the range is 50.

Rate

A comparison of two different quantities.

e.g. **60 km/h**

Ratio

The comparison of one number to another by division [see pp. 70–71].

e.g. The ratio of 3 to 4 can be expressed as $^3/_4$ or as 3:4

Rational number

Any number that can be expressed as a fraction [see pp. 70–71].

e.g. $3 = {}^3/_1$ $3.7 = {}^{37}/_{10}$ $2^1/_4 = {}^9/_4$

Ray (Half-line)

Part of a line with one end point.

e.g.

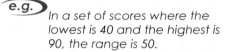

Real number

Any number that can be represented on the number line; i.e. all rational numbers (such as $^3/_4$) and all irrational numbers (such as √2). [√−1 is an example of an 'unreal' or imaginary number. See p. 71.]

Reciprocal (Inverse)

The product of a number and its reciprocal is one.

e.g. $^2/_3$ is the reciprocal of $^3/_2$ and vice versa; and the reciprocal of any number n is $^1/_n$.

Rectangle

A quadrilateral with all angles right angles [see p. 93].

Rectangular numbers (Composite numbers)

Numbers that can be represented by objects in a rectangular array; e.g. 6 and 15 are rectangular numbers, as shown.

Recurring decimal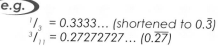

A decimal where one or more digits continually repeat.

$$\frac{1}{3} = 0.3333... \text{ (shortened to } 0.\overline{3})$$
$$\frac{3}{11} = 0.27272727... (0.\overline{27})$$

Reduction

A decrease in the size of an object or figure while maintaining the same shape; e.g. the letter W has been reduced here [see p. 103].

Reflection (Flip)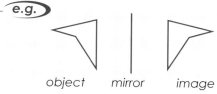

The mirror image of an object or figure, where each point of the object is the same distance from the 'mirror line' as its corresponding point on the image [see p. 102].

object   mirror   image

Reflex angle

An angle of size greater than a straight angle of 180° and less than a revolution of 360° [see p. 86].

Region

Part of a plane (2-D) or part of space (3-D); e.g. an elliptical region; a cubic region.

Regular polygon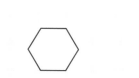

Any polygon with all sides congruent and all angles congruent; e.g. the one shown here is a regular hexagon [see p. 87].

Regular polyhedron (Regular solid)

[See Platonic solids]

List of mathematical terms

Remainder   *e.g.*

The number remaining after a division of whole numbers.

When dividing 10 by 3 the remainder is 1.

Repeated addition   *e.g.*

An addition strategy to help solve multiplication equations.

$3 + 3 + 3 + 3 = 4 \times 3$

Revolution

One complete turn through 360 degrees.

Rhombus   *e.g.*

A parallelogram with four congruent sides [often incorrectly called a diamond; see p. 92.]

Right angle   *e.g.*

An angle of size 90 degrees, usually marked as shown.

Right-angled triangle   *e.g.*

A triangle with one right angle [see pp. 88–89].

Roman numerals   *e.g.*

Ancient system of numeration where numbers are represented by letters of the Roman alphabet; i.e. the numerals are formed from a combination of the symbols I (1), V (5), X (10), L (50), C (100), D (500), and M (1000); [see p. 62].

CLXIV = 164

Root   *e.g.*

The base of a power.

In $2^3 = 8$, the cube root of 8 is 2, shown as $\sqrt[3]{8} = 2$.

Root of an equation   *e.g.*

The number that satisfies the equation; also called the solution of the equation.

$y = 2$ is the root or solution of the equation, $3y + 2 = 8$.

Rotation (Turn)   *e.g.*

The process by which an object or figure changes position by rotating about a fixed point through a given angle [see p. 102].

The minute hand on a clock rotates about the centre of the clock face in a clockwise direction through 90° every quarter hour.

Rotational symmetry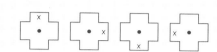

An object or figure has rotational symmetry if it appears to retain its original orientation after rotating through some fraction of a complete turn about a fixed point; e.g. the figure shown has rotational symmetry of order 4. [See also Order of rotational symmetry and see p. 101.]

Rounding

Expressing a number to the nearest specified place value. [Note that 4975 can be rounded to either 4970 or 4980 depending on the context.]

4873 rounded to the nearest:
ten is   4870
hundred is   4900
thousand is   5000

Row

An arrangement of objects in a horizontal line [see Array].

S

Sample

[See Random sample]

Scale

The ratio of measurements of a model or diagram to corresponding measurements of an enlarged or reduced version.

If the scale on a map is 1:100 000 then 1 cm on the map represents 100 000 cm (1 km) at the actual location.

Scale factor

See Scale, above. While scale is expressed in 1-D, the factor is squared when relating to area (2-D) and cubed for volume (3-D); e.g. for cubes A and B the linear (1-D) scale factor is 1:2, the area (2-D) scale factor is 1:4, and the volume (3-D) scale factor is 1:8.

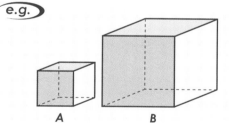

A   B

Scalene triangle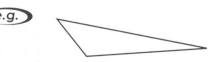

A triangle with no sides congruent. [From the Greek *skalenos* meaning 'uneven'. See pp. 88–89.]

Scales

Instruments used for comparing or measuring masses; the main types being a beam balance, spring-based scales and electronic scales.

Scattergram (Scatter plot) **e.g.**

Short for 'scatter diagram'; a graph of plotted points which display the relationship between two sets of data; e.g. this graph shows that arm span and height are highly correlated [see p. 84].

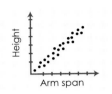

Scientific notation **e.g.**

A shortened way of writing very large or very small numbers.

$$4\ 700\ 000 = 4.7 \times 1\ 000\ 000 = 4.7 \times 10^6$$
$$0.0000025 = 2.5 \times 0.000001 = 2.5 \times 10^{-6}$$

Score

A value in statistics, and also a name for 20. [From Old Norse *skor* meaning a 'notch' or 'tally mark', and with marks grouped in 20s this led to the use of it as a name for 20.]

Season **e.g.**

There are four seasons in one year.

spring, summer, autumn, winter

Second (s)

A unit of time or angle measure [60 seconds = 1 minute]; or position number two in order. [See Ordinal number.]

Sector **e.g.**

Portion of a circular region bounded by two radii and an arc [see p. 95].

This figure shows two sectors.

Semicircle **e.g.**

Half a circle; e.g. any diameter divides a circle into two semicircles as shown. [*Semi* is from Latin for 'half'; see p. 95.]

Sequence (Series) **e.g.**

A set of objects, figures or numbers arranged in a given order.

3, 6, 9, 12, 15, … is the sequence of multiples of 3.

Seriate

[See Ordering]

Set **e.g.**

A well-defined collection.

The set of square numbers less than 10 is {1, 4, 9}.

SI

The international system of measurement units derived from the metric system and using the base units of metre, kilogram, second, ampere, candela, kelvin and mole. [SI is the universal symbol for the French title *Système Internationale d'Unités*; see pp. 106–108.]

List of mathematical terms

Side

A line segment forming part of a polygon.

 An octagon has eight sides.

Significant figure

The digit in a numeral that indicates the size of the number to a certain degree of accuracy. [See p. 112 for examples of the use of conversion factors with four significant figures.]

 In 359 the 3 is the most significant figure.

Similar triangles

Triangles of the same shape but differing in size [see p. 90].

Slope

[See Gradient]

Speed

Distance travelled per unit of time.

 60 km/h

Sphere

A 3-D shape with one curved surface, where every point on that surface is the same distance from the sphere's centre.

• a tennis ball is a model of a sphere
• the Earth is almost spherical

Spinner

A device for randomly selecting a value or attribute.

 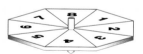

Square

A rectangle with four congruent sides [see p. 93].

The result of multiplying a number by itself. [See Square number and p. 63.]

The square of 3 is 9; $3^2 = 9$.

Square centimetre (cm²)

A unit of area equivalent to that contained in a square region with sides of length 1 cm. [The region shown is about 1 cm² in size.]

 1 cm 1 cm

Square kilometre (km²)

A unit of area equivalent to that contained in a square region with sides of length 1 km.

Square metre (m²)

A unit of area equivalent to that contained in a square region with sides of length 1 m.

Square number

e.g.

Any counting number obtained by multiplying a number by itself; i.e. 1, 4, 9, 16, ... are the square numbers. [A square number of objects can be placed in a square array as shown; see p. 63.]

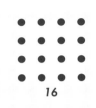

16

Square root (√)

e.g.

The opposite of squaring a number.

The square root of 9 is 3 because $3^2 = 9$ and it is written as $\sqrt{9} = 3$.

Statistics

The study concerned with the collection and classification of numerical facts called data, which may be represented in tables or graphs for interpretation and analysis.

Stem and leaf plot

e.g.

A means of displaying data whereby the numbers in the data are split into two parts to show the range and spread of data; e.g. the data 21, 19, 34, 16, 27, 35, 19, 26, 24, 28, 32 may be displayed in a stem and leaf plot as shown [see p. 85].

Stem	Leaves
1	9 6 9
2	1 7 6 4 8
3	4 5 2

Stone

An Imperial unit of weight that remains in common usage. One stone is approximately 6.35 kg.

Straight angle

e.g.

An angle of size 180° [see p. 86].

Subitise

e.g.

Mentally grouping sets of items so that the number of each group can be recognised without counting; e.g. in Set A it can be seen that there are 5 objects without counting; while in Set B a subset of 4 and another subset of 5 can be seen, giving a total of 9 without counting.

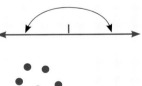

Subset

e.g.

A set within a set.

The set of even numbers is a subset of the set of counting numbers.

Subtract (−)

A numerical operation involving 'taking away' or 'finding the difference' or 'finding the complement'.

e.g.

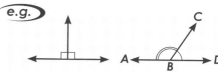

$$10 - 6 = ?$$
$$6 + ? = 10$$

Sum

The result of adding two or more numbers [see Addition].

e.g.

The sum of 8 and 9 is 17, since 9 + 8 = 17.

Supplementary angles

Two angles which together make 180°; e.g. two right angles are supplementary; angles ABC and CBD are supplementary.

e.g.

Surface

The outside of something, and can be either a planar surface (2-D) or a curved surface (3-D); e.g. the base and top of a cylinder are plane surfaces, while the remainder is a curved surface.

e.g.

Symbol

A letter, numeral or mark that represents something [see p. 116].

e.g.

$8, +, -, x, ÷, g, =, \%, >$
are all symbols.

Symmetry

The correspondence—in size, form, and arrangement—of parts on opposite sides of a point, line or plane; e.g. the triangle shown is symmetrical about the vertical line. [This is reflection symmetry. See also Rotational symmetry and p. 101]

e.g.

T

Table

A means of organising data in rows and columns for a particular purpose; e.g. this table shows the number of Jen's and Ryan's red and blue socks.

e.g.

	Red socks	Blue socks
Jen	2	6
Ryan	6	8

Tally marks

Marks made to record items or events, usually grouped in fives by a diagonal stroke [see p. 77].

e.g.

The diagram shows a tally of 14 objects.

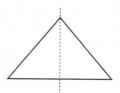

Tangent
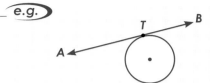

A line that intersects a curve at one point; e.g. the line AB is a tangent to the circle shown at point T. [From the Latin *tangere* meaning 'to touch'; see p. 95.]

Tangram
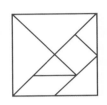

The name of an ancient Chinese square puzzle consisting of seven pieces (five right-angled triangles, a square, and a parallelogram as shown) that can be rearranged to make various shapes.

Teens number
e.g.

A number with the suffix '–teen'.

thirteen, fourteen, fifteen, sixteen, seventeen, eighteen, nineteen

Terminating decimal
e.g.

When a rational number (which can always be named by a fraction) is expressed as a decimal, the result will be either a terminating decimal with a finite number of places, or a recurring decimal with an infinite number of places. [See also Recurring decimal.]

$^3/_8 = 3 \div 8 = 0.375$, which is a terminating decimal.

Tessellating (Tiling)

Completely covering a plane surface with one or more shapes without gaps or overlapping; e.g. all triangles and quadrilaterals are tessellating shapes. [From the Latin *tessera* meaning 'a square tablet'.]

Tetrahedron (Triangular pyramid)

A polyhedron with four triangular faces [see pp. 98–99].

Three-dimensional (3-D)

[See Dimension]

Timetable
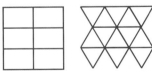

A list or table of events arranged according to the time when they take place.

Time	Event
9.00 a.m.	Meet and greet
9.15 a.m.	Presentation 1
10.15 a.m.	Coffee break
10.45 a.m.	Presentation 2
12.15 p.m.	Lunch

Tonne (t)

A unit of mass equivalent to 1000 kg. [Not to be confused with ton which is an imperial measure of about 1016 kg.]

Topology.

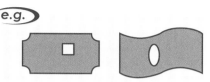

A branch of geometry concerned with the properties of figures that are independent of measurement; i.e. the properties remain the same even when the figure is stretched or distorted. [Topology is often called 'rubber sheet geometry'.]

The two figures shown are topologically the same as they both have one hole.

Total

The complete sum of a number of parts.

50 + 40 totals 90

Transformation

The process by which an object or figure is changed in shape, size or position. [See Enlargement, Reduction, Reflection, Rotation, Translation, and Distortion; and see pp. 102–103.]

Translation (Slide)

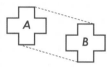

The process by which an object or figure changes position, without turning, for a given distance in a given direction [see p. 102].

Figure B is a slide image of Figure A and vice versa.

Transversal

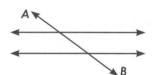

A line which intersects two or more parallel lines; e.g. the line AB is a transversal since it intersects two parallel lines [see p. 86].

Trapezium (Trapezoid)

A quadrilateral with only one pair of parallel sides. [From the Greek *trapeza* meaning 'table'. See p. 92.]

Traversable (Unicursal)

Applies to a network and means that by starting at a point, all the paths of the network can be traversed once only; e.g. network A is traversable but network B is not.

Tree diagram

A diagram using a branching process to solve a problem; e.g. to find the prime factors of 12 [see p. 85].

Triangle

A three-sided polygon [see pp. 88–91].

Triangular number

A number that can be represented by objects or symbols arranged in the shape of a triangle; i.e. 1, 3, 6, 10, 15, ... [see p. 63].

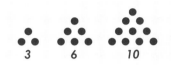

Trigonometry

A branch of mathematics concerned with the relationships between the angles and the sides of triangles [see p. 91].

Trillion

A million million; i.e. 1 000 000 000 000 or 10^{12} [see p. 61].

Trundle wheel

A wheel, usually with a circumference of one metre, used for measuring distances. [A very much smaller wheel is used for measuring distances on a map.]

Two-dimensional (2-D)

[See Dimension]

U

Unequal

[See Not equal]

Unicursal

[See Traversable]

Unit

e.g.

Another name for one.

Units is a place value in the numeration system.

The particular standard used in all measurements.

The SI units for length are mm, cm, m, km.

Unitary method

A simple way of solving certain numerical problems by finding the value of a unit.

What is 7% of 240?
Find the value of a unit percentage: 1% of 240 is 2.40. So 7% of 240 is 7 x 2.40, which is 16.80.

Universal set (U)

The set of all members being considered.

 e.g.

If the odd and even numbers are being considered then the universal set for this case could be the set of all whole numbers, or the set of all rational numbers etc.

 V

Variable

A quantity that can change its values, usually represented by a single letter.

 e.g.

In the equation $x + y = 10$, x and y are variables while 10 is a constant.

Velocity

Speed in a particular direction.

Venn diagram

A diagram that represents sets and their relationships; e.g. the two sets shown are the set of square numbers from 1 to 9 (Set A) and the set of even numbers from 1 to 9 (Set B). [Named after John Venn who developed the method in the 1890s. See p. 77.]

e.g.

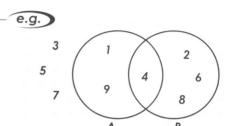

Vertex

The common point of the two rays of an angle; e.g. vertex A as shown.

The point of intersection of two sides of a polygon, or of three or more faces or edges of a three-dimensional figure; e.g. as at vertices B and C respectively.

e.g.

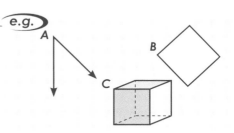

Vertical

The direction of a plumb line; i.e. upright and perpendicular to the horizontal.

Vertically opposite angles

The two pairs of angles formed by the intersection of two lines; e.g. a & b which are congruent and c & d which are congruent [see p. 86].

e.g.

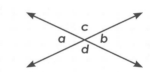

List of mathematical terms

Vinculum (–)

The horizontal dash or 'fraction line' separating the numerator and denominator of a fraction and which indicates division. [The forward slash '/' is also used for the same purpose, as in $^3/_4$].

e.g.

The '–' separating the 3 and the 4 in the fraction,

so that $\dfrac{3}{4} = 3 \div 4 = 0.75$

Volume

The amount of space occupied. [See also Capacity, and pp. 114–115.]

Week

A unit of time consisting of seven days [see p. 109].

Weight

The force of gravity acting on an object, used to measure mass. [Weight is measured in Newtons, named after the great mathematician Isaac Newton, who developed the laws of gravity.]

Whole number

[See Cardinal number]

Width

[See Breadth]

x-axis & y-axis

[See Coordinates]

Yard

An imperial unit of length equivalent to about 91 cm.

Year

The time it takes the Earth to revolve around the sun and set at 365 days for a normal year and 366 days in a leap year. [The exact time is 365 days, 5 hours, 48 minutes, 45 seconds. See p. 110.]

Z

Zero (0)

The cardinal number of the empty set is 0; i.e. the first whole number. [Note that zero has special properties and so, like one, is considered a special number.]

Additional information

Tables

Number systems

Charts

2-D shapes

3-D shapes

Measurement systems

Conversion tables

Equivalences

Formulas

Rules

Explanations

Symbols

Addition and subtraction table

+	0	1	2	3	4	5	6	7	8	9
0	0	1	2	3	4	5	6	7	8	9
1	1	2	3	4	5	6	7	8	9	10
2	2	3	4	5	6	7	8	9	10	11
3	3	4	5	6	7	8	9	10	11	12
4	4	5	6	7	8	9	10	11	12	13
5	5	6	7	8	9	10	11	12	13	14
6	6	7	8	9	10	11	12	13	14	15
7	7	8	9	10	11	12	13	14	15	16
8	8	9	10	11	12	13	14	15	16	17
9	9	10	11	12	13	14	15	16	17	18

Using the table

For example, to find the sum 8 + 5 = 13, go along Row 8 and come down Column 5 to meet at 13 in the shaded area. To find the sum 5 + 8, go along Row 5 and come down Column 8 to get to 13 in the unshaded area.

Notice that the unshaded area has the same set of sums as on the shaded side of the diagonal, so the unshaded part of the table is not needed, because changing the order of addition still gives the same result; e.g. 8 + 5 = 5 + 8.

Because addition and subtraction are opposite operations, the table also shows all the subtraction facts.

Except for the diagonal, every number in the table shows a family of four facts in one; e.g. 13 shows 8 + 5 = 13, 5 + 8 = 13, 13 – 5 = 8, and 13 – 8 = 5. Numbers in the diagonal show only two facts; e.g. 7 + 7 = 14, and 14 – 7 = 7.

X	0	1	2	3	4	5	6	7	8	9
0	0	0	0	0	0	0	0	0	0	0
1	0	1	2	3	4	5	6	7	8	9
2	0	2	4	6	8	10	12	14	16	18
3	0	3	6	9	12	15	18	21	24	27
4	0	4	8	12	16	20	24	28	32	36
5	0	5	10	15	20	25	30	35	40	45
6	0	6	12	18	24	30	36	42	48	54
7	0	7	14	21	28	35	42	49	56	63
8	0	8	16	24	32	40	48	56	64	72
9	0	9	18	27	36	45	54	63	72	81

Using the table

For example, to find the product 8 x 5 = 40, go along Row 8 and come down Column 5 to meet at 40 in the shaded area. To find the product 5 x 8, go along Row 5 and come down Column 8 to get to 40 in the unshaded area.

Notice that the unshaded area has the same set of products as on the shaded side of the diagonal, so the unshaded part of the table is not needed, because changing the order of multiplication still gives the same result; e.g. 8 x 5 = 5 x 8.

Because multiplication and division are inverse operations, the table also shows all the division facts.

Except for the diagonal, every number in the table shows a family of four facts in one; e.g. 40 shows 8 x 5 = 40, 5 x 8 = 40, 40 ÷ 5 = 8, and 40 ÷ 8 = 5. Numbers in the diagonal show only two facts; e.g. 7 x 7 = 49, and 49 ÷ 7 = 7.

Basic properties of the operations

Commutative property of addition
e.g.
Numbers may be added in any order without affecting the sum. [This almost halves the number of basic addition and subtraction facts to be learned. See p. 58.]

$$7 + 3 = 3 + 7$$

Commutative property of multiplication
e.g.
Numbers may be multiplied in any order without affecting the product. [This almost halves the number of basic multiplication and division facts to be learned. See p. 59.]

$$7 \times 3 = 3 \times 7$$

Associative property of addition
e.g.
When adding three or more numbers, the grouping does not affect the sum. [So columns of numbers can be added up or down, or added in convenient groups.]

$$2 + (3 + 4) = (2 + 3) + 4$$

Associative property of multiplication
e.g.
When multiplying three or more numbers, the grouping does not affect the product. [So numbers can be multiplied in convenient groups.]

$$2 \times (3 \times 4) = (2 \times 3) \times 4$$

Distributive property of multiplication over addition
e.g.
Multiplication may be spread over addition. [This is handy when multiplying larger numbers; e.g. $5 \times 967 = (5 \times 900) + (5 \times 60) + (5 \times 7)$.]

$$2 \times (3 + 7) = (2 \times 3) + (2 \times 7)$$

Addition property of zero
e.g.
The sum of any number and zero is that number. [Zero is said to be the 'identity element' in addition.]

$$7 + 0 = 7$$

Multiplication property of zero
e.g.
The product of any number and zero is zero.

$$7 \times 0 = 0$$

Multiplication property of one
e.g.
The product of any number and one is that number. [One is said to be the 'identity element' in multiplication. Note how this property is used to generate equivalent fractions: $\frac{1}{2} = \frac{1}{2} \times 1 = \frac{1}{2} \times \frac{5}{5} = \frac{5}{10}$]

$$7 \times 1 = 7$$

The decimal system of numeration uses the ten digits 0, 1, 2, 3, 4, 5, 6, 7, 8, and 9 in a place value system. Each place in the system has a value ten times the value of the place on its right and one-tenth the value of the place on its left. All place values are powers of ten. Any rational number, no matter how large or how small, can be represented in the system. The places are grouped in threes as shown below to assist in reading the number names.

Hundreds of quadrillions	18	
Tens of quadrillions	17	VI. Quadrillions
Quadrillions	16	

Hundreds of trillions	15	
Tens of trillions	14	V. Trillions
Trillions	13	

Hundreds of billions	12	
Tens of billions	11	IV. Billions
Billions	10	

Hundreds of millions	9	
Tens of millions	8	III. Millions
Millions	7	

Hundreds of thousands	6	
Tens of thousands	5	II. Thousands
Thousands	4	

Hundreds	3	
Tens	2	I. Units
Units	1	

●

Hundreds of thousandths	1	
Tens of thousandths	2	1. Thousandths
Thousandths	3	

Hundreds of millionths	4	
Tens of millionths	5	2. Millionths
Millionths	6	

By using the triple groupings, the numeral 12 406 791 covers the place values of three sections—millions, thousands and units—and is read in three parts as 'twelve million, four hundred and six thousand, seven hundred and ninety-one'.

Place values to the right of the units or ones place are to represent numbers that are not integers. The number represented in the diagram below is 2146.358, with the dot being a marker called a 'decimal point' to separate the ones from the tenths. In reality, 2146.358 means 'two thousand one hundred and forty-six, and three hundred and fifty-eight one-thousandths', but is read more briefly as 'two thousand, one hundred and forty-six, point three five eight'. The word 'point' may also be read as 'decimal'.

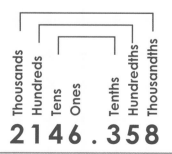

Roman numeration system and Greek alphabet

Roman letters used in numeration

Symbols used both in the Roman system of numeration and in our Hindu-Arabic system of numeration are shown below.

Roman	I	V	X	L	C	D	M
Hindu-Arabic	1	5	10	50	100	500	1000

Rules for using the Roman system

1. All symbols for decimal place values may be repeated up to three times.

   e.g.
   III = 1 + 1 + 1 = 3;
   XXX = 10 + 10 + 10 = 30;
   CCC = 100 + 100 + 100 = 300;
   MMM = 1000 + 1000 + 1000 = 3000.

2. A lesser value symbol in front of a greater value symbol means the lesser value is subtracted.

   e.g.
   IV = 5 – 1 = 4;
   IX = 10 – 1 = 9;
   XL = 50 – 10 = 40;
   CD = 500 – 100 = 400.

3. Lesser value symbols following a greater value symbol means the lesser value(s) is/are added.

   e.g.
   VI = 5 + 1 = 6;
   XV = 10 + 5 = 15;
   LXIII = 50 + 10 + 3 = 63;
   CXXXI = 100 + 10 + 10 + 10 + 1 = 131.

Letters from the Greek alphabet used in maths

Many of the letters of the Greek alphabet are used in mathematics as special symbols. For example, *pi* (π) is used to represent the ratio of the circumference to the diameter of any circle. The list below includes both upper and lower cases of the Greek letters. [The word *alphabet* comes from the first two Greek letters, *alpha* & *beta*.]

Greek	Name	English	Greek	Name	English
A α	alpha	a	N ν	nu	n
B β	beta	b	Π π	pi	p
Γ γ	gamma	g	P ρ	rho	r
Δ δ	delta	d	Σ σ	sigma	s
E ε	epsilon	e	T τ	tau	t
Θ θ	theta	th	Y υ	upsilon	u
I ι	iota	i	Φ φ	phi	ph
Λ λ	lambda	l	X χ	chi	ch
M μ	mu	m	Ω ω	omega	o

Figurative numbers are numbers that can be represented by arrangements of regular polygons that grow proportionally, starting at 1. By following the patterns, each set of figurative numbers can be extended as far as required.

Triangular numbers

Triangular numbers are those that can be represented by objects or symbols arranged in the shape of a triangle.

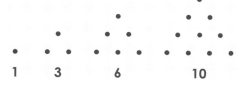

1   3   6   10

These can also be shown in two other ways:

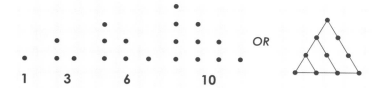

1   3   6   10   OR

Square numbers

Square numbers are those obtained by multiplying a number by itself, and can be represented by objects or symbols arranged in the shape of a square.

1   4   9   16

These can also be shown as:

Relationship between triangular numbers and square numbers

When any two consecutive triangular numbers are joined, they form a square number; e.g. 6 + 3 = 9.

6 + 3 = 9

Figurative numbers

Pentagonal numbers

Pentagonal numbers are those that can be represented by objects or symbols arranged in the shape of a pentagon.

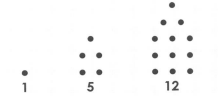

1   5   12

These can also be shown as:

Relationship between pentagonal numbers and triangular and square numbers

Pentagonal numbers are a union of the triangular and square numbers.

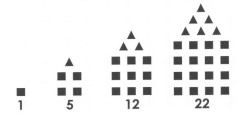

1   5   12   22

Hexagonal numbers

Hexagonal numbers are those that can be represented by objects or symbols arranged in the shape of a hexagon.

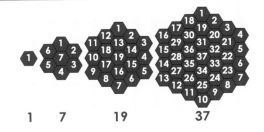

1   7   19   37

These can also be shown as:

Any counting number that divides another without any remainder is a factor of that number; e.g. 1, 2, 3, 5, 6, 10, 15 and 30 are factors of 30 because 1 x 30 = 30; 2 x 15 = 30; 3 x 10 = 30, and 5 x 6 = 30; i.e. they all divide 30 without any remainder.

A prime number that divides a given counting number without any remainder is called a prime factor. In the above example, 2, 3 and 5 are prime factors of 30. [Note that 1 is not considered a prime number.]

Finding prime factors

1. Use a factor tree.

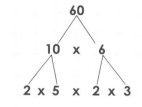

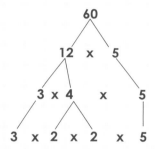

2. Divide by prime numbers and continue as much as possible.

$$2 \overline{)60}$$
$$2 \overline{)30}$$
$$3 \overline{)15}$$
$$5$$

Thus 60 = 2 x 2 x 3 x 5, so the prime factors of 60 are 2, 3, and 5

Factors and rectangular numbers

All counting numbers can be represented by arrangements of objects or symbols in arrays, and the arrays show the factors of the numbers. Prime numbers have only two arrays and have only two factors, whereas composite numbers have more than two arrays and have more than two factors. Also, square numbers can be seen to form a square array. The arrays for the first 12 counting numbers are shown below and on the following page.

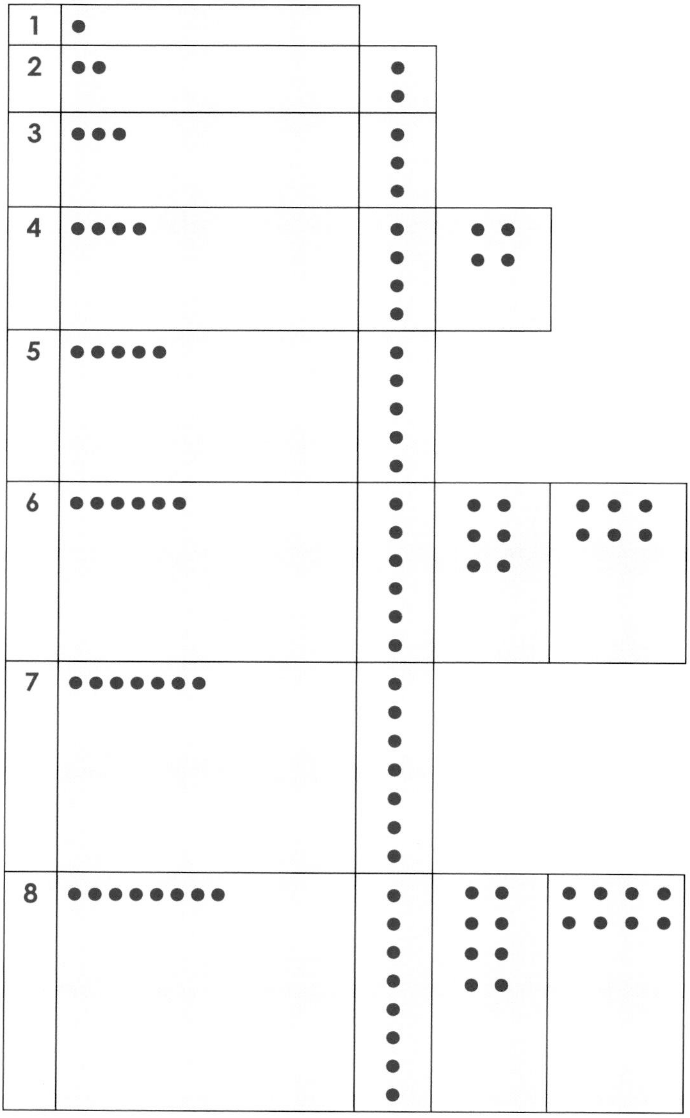

1	●		
2	● ●	● ● (vertical)	
3	● ● ●	● ● ● (vertical)	
4	● ● ● ●	● ● ● ● (vertical)	● ● / ● ●
5	● ● ● ● ●	● ● ● ● ● (vertical)	
6	● ● ● ● ● ●	● ● ● ● ● ● (vertical)	● ● / ● ● / ● ● and ● ● ● / ● ● ●
7	● ● ● ● ● ● ●	● ● ● ● ● ● ● (vertical)	
8	● ● ● ● ● ● ● ●	● ● ● ● ● ● ● ● (vertical)	● ● / ● ● / ● ● / ● ● and ● ● ● ● / ● ● ● ●

9	••••••••	• • • • • • • • •	• • • • • • • • •		
10	••••••••••	• • • • • • • • •	(2 × 5 array)	(5 × 2 array)	
11	•••••••••••	• • • • • • • • • • •			
12	••••••••••••	• • • • • • • • • • • •	(2 × 6 array)	(6 × 2 array)	(3 × 4 array)	(4 × 3 array)

Prime and composite numbers to 200

The prime numbers are shown in black. The others are composite numbers, but 1 is a special number and is neither prime nor composite.

1	**2**	**3**	4	**5**	6	**7**	8	9	10
11	12	**13**	14	15	16	**17**	18	**19**	20
21	22	**23**	24	25	26	27	28	**29**	30
31	32	33	34	35	36	**37**	38	39	40
41	42	**43**	44	45	46	**47**	48	49	50
51	52	**53**	54	55	56	57	58	**59**	60
61	62	63	64	65	66	**67**	68	69	70
71	72	**73**	74	75	76	77	78	**79**	80
81	82	**83**	84	85	86	87	88	**89**	90
91	92	93	94	95	96	**97**	98	99	100
101	102	**103**	104	105	106	**107**	108	**109**	110
111	112	**113**	114	115	116	117	118	119	120
121	122	123	124	125	126	**127**	128	129	130
131	132	133	134	135	136	**137**	138	**139**	140
141	142	143	144	145	146	147	148	**149**	150
151	152	153	154	155	156	**157**	158	159	160
161	162	**163**	164	165	166	**167**	168	169	170
171	172	**173**	174	175	176	177	178	**179**	180
181	182	183	184	185	186	187	188	189	190
191	192	**193**	194	195	196	**197**	198	**199**	200

The Complete Handbook of Maths Terms   www.prim-ed.com   Prim-Ed Publishing

Rules for divisibility

Number	Rule
Two	All even numbers are divisible by 2; i.e. the last digit is 0, 2, 4, 6, or 8; e.g. 70, 240, 3 964 and 11 486 are even numbers so they are all divisible by 2.
Three	The sum of the digits of the number is divisible by 3; e.g. 1 + 9 + 2 = 12, which is divisible by 3, so 192 is divisible by 3.
Four	The number represented by the last two digits of the number is divisible by 4; e.g. 28 is divisible by 4, so 528, 3228 and 13 028 are all divisible by four.
Five	The last digit of the number is either 0 or 5; e.g. 65, 740, 935 and 3890 all end in either 0 or 5 so they are all divisible by 5.
Six	The number is even and the sum of its digits is divisible by 3; e.g. 732 is even and 7 + 3 + 2 = 12 which is divisible by 3, so 732 is divisible by 6.
Seven	There is no simple rule.
Eight	The number represented by the last three digits is divisible by 8; e.g. 936 is divisible by 8, so 5936, 24 936 and 125 936 are all divisible by 8.
Nine	The sum of the digits of the number add to 9; e.g. for 738, 7 + 3 + 8 = 18, and 1 + 8 = 9, so 738 is divisible by 9.
Ten	The last digit of the number is 0; e.g. 90, 170 and 3710 all end in 0 so they are all divisible by 10.
Twenty	The last digit is 0 and the tens digit is even; e.g. 120, 780, 3040 and 17 960 all end in 0 and have an even tens digit so they are all divisible by 20.

Rational number equivalents

Fraction	Decimal	Percent	Ratio
$^1/_1$	1	100%	1:1
$^1/_2$	0.5	50%	1:2
$^1/_3$	$0.\overline{3}$	$33.\overline{3}$%	1:3
$^2/_3$	$0.\overline{6}$	$66.\overline{6}$%	2:3
$^1/_4$	0.25	25%	1:4
$^3/_4$	0.75	75%	3:4
$^1/_5$	0.2	20%	1:5
$^2/_5$	0.4	40%	2:5
$^3/_5$	0.6	60%	3:5
$^4/_5$	0.8	80%	4:5
$^1/_6$	$0.1\overline{6}$	$16.\overline{6}$%	1:6
$^5/_6$	$0.8\overline{3}$	$83.\overline{3}$%	5:6
$^1/_8$	0.125	12.5%	1:8
$^3/_8$	0.375	37.5%	3:8
$^5/_8$	0.625	62.5%	5:8
$^7/_8$	0.875	87.5%	7:8
$^1/_{10}$	0.1	10%	1:10
$^3/_{10}$	0.3	30%	3:10
$^7/_{10}$	0.7	70%	7:10
$^9/_{10}$	0.9	90%	9:10
$^1/_{12}$	$0.08\overline{3}$	$8.\overline{3}$%	1:12
$^1/_{20}$	0.05	5%	1:20
$^1/_{25}$	0.04	4%	1:25
$^1/_{40}$	0.025	2.5%	1:40
$^1/_{50}$	0.02	2%	1:50
$^1/_{100}$	0.01	1%	1:100
$^1/_{1000}$	0.001	0.1%	1:1000
$^1/_{10000}$	0.0001	0.01%	1:10 000
$^{67}/_{100}$	0.67	67%	67:100

The Complete Handbook of Maths Terms   www.prim-ed.com   Prim-Ed Publishing

The chart below classifies all numbers. The first numbers used are *counting numbers* {1, 2, 3, ...}, then these with *zero* make up the *whole numbers* {0, 1, 2, 3, ...}. The whole numbers together with their opposites, ⁻1, ⁻2, ⁻3, ... make up the set of *integers* {... ⁻3, ⁻2, ⁻1, 0, 1, 2, 3, ...}. Then there are the *non-integer rational numbers* such as $\frac{3}{4}$, $\frac{-3}{4}$, $\frac{7}{5}$, and $\frac{-7}{5}$; that together with the whole numbers form the set of all *rational numbers*. Then there are the *irrational numbers*, such as $\sqrt{2}$, $-\sqrt{2}$, π, $-\pi$ to complete the set of all *real numbers*.

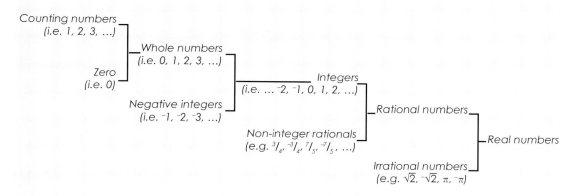

Note: Rational numbers are based on ratio and are all numbers resulting from the division of any integer by any other integer except 0. Thus all rational numbers can be represented by a fraction, while irrational numbers cannot be expressed in this way but are still represented on the number line; e.g. note how $\sqrt{2}$ is located there. Thus the set of real numbers fills all points on the number line.

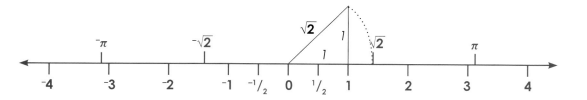

Indices

A quick way of writing 3 x 3 x 3 x 3 is 3^4. In this case 3 is called the base, and 4 is called the index (power, exponent). The index indicates the power to which the base has been raised. The numeral 3^4 is read as 'three raised to the power four', or as 'three to the fourth power', or more briefly as 'three to the fourth'. The plural for 'index' is 'indices' or 'indexes'. The index rules for multiplication and division are detailed below.

Index law	Example	General rule
Multiplication		
When multiplying powers with the same base, add the indices.	$3^2 = 3 \times 3$ $3^4 = 3 \times 3 \times 3 \times 3$ $3^2 \times 3^4 = 3 \times 3 \times 3 \times 3 \times 3 \times 3$ $= 3^6$ $= 3^{2+4}$	If a is any real number and m and n are positive integers, then $$a^m \times a^n = a^{m+n}$$
Division		
When dividing powers of the same base, the index of the denominator is subtracted from the index of the numerator.	$\dfrac{3^6}{3^2} = \dfrac{3 \times 3 \times 3 \times 3 \times 3 \times 3}{3 \times 3}$ $= 3^{6-2}$ $= 3^4$	If a is any real number and m and n are positive integers, then $$\dfrac{a^m}{a^n} = a^{m-n}$$
Power of zero		
Any real number, except 0, raised to the power zero has a value of 1.	$\dfrac{3^4}{3^4} = 3^{4-4}$ $= 3^0$ $= 1$	If a is any real number but $a \neq 0$, then $$a^0 = 1$$
Power raised to powers		
When a power of a number is raised to another power, multiply the indices.	$(3^2)^3 = (3 \times 3)^3$ $= 3 \times 3 \times 3 \times 3 \times 3 \times 3$ $= 3^{2 \times 3}$ $= 3^6$	If a is any real number and m and n are positive integers, then $$(a^m)^n = a^{mn}$$

Index law	Example	General rule
Powers of products		
When a product is raised to a power, every factor of the product is raised to that power.	$(3 \times 5)^2 = (3 \times 5) \times (3 \times 5)$ $= 3^2 \times 5^2$	If a and b are any real numbers and n is a positive integer, then $(ab)^n = a^n b^n$
Powers of quotients		
When a quotient is raised to a power, both the numerator and the denominator are raised to that power.	$(\frac{3}{5})^3 = \frac{3}{5} \times \frac{3}{5} \times \frac{3}{5}$ $= \frac{3^3}{5^3}$	If a and b are any real numbers, but $b \neq 0$, and n is a positive integer, then $(\frac{a}{b})^n = \frac{a^n}{b^n}$
Negative powers		
Raising any real number except 0 to a negative power results in the reciprocal.	$3^{-2} = \frac{1}{3^2}$	If a is any real number, but $a \neq 0$, and n is a positive integer, then $a^{-n} = \frac{1}{a^n}$
Fractional powers		
The denominator of the fraction indicates the root.	$5^{\frac{2}{3}} = \sqrt[3]{5^2}$	If a is any real number and m and n are positive integers, then $a^{\frac{m}{n}} = \sqrt[n]{a^m}$

Maths in finance

Simple interest

Simple interest (SI) is the amount of money paid on an invested amount called the principal (P), calculated at an annual percentage rate (R), and paid at the end of a period of time (T) expressed in years.

To find the simple interest on £800 invested at seven percent for two years:

$$SI = P \times R \times T$$
$$= £800 \times 7\% \times 2$$
$$= £112$$

Compound interest

Compound interest (CI) is when the interest earned on an investment is added to the principal each year, thus increasing the return year by year.

To find the compound interest on €800 invested at seven percent for two years:

$$CI = P \times (1 + R)^T - P$$
$$= €800 \times (1 + 0.07)^2 - €800$$
$$= €800 \times (1.07)^2 - €800$$
$$= €915.92 - €800$$
$$= €115.92$$

Commission

A commission (C) is a payment made for a service and calculated as a percentage of the total amount of the transaction.

If a car salesperson is paid 2% commission on selling a car for £12 000, this is calculated as follows:

$$C = 2\% \text{ of } £12\ 000$$
$$= 2\% \times £12\ 000$$
$$= £240$$

Discount

A discount is the amount taken off the price of an item and is expressed either as an amount of money or as a percentage off the marked price.

If the marked price of an item is €48 and the discount is 10%, the amount of money taken off is calculated as follows:

$$\text{Discount} = 10\% \text{ of } €48$$
$$= 10\% \times €48$$
$$= €4.80$$
$$\text{Final selling price} = €48 - €4.80 = €43.20$$

Maths in finance

Profit and loss

Profit is the amount of money gained in a transaction or over a certain period of time, such as a year; while if this amount is negative it is called a loss. Profit can be expressed both as an amount of money and as a percentage of the transaction(s).

 e.g.

For example, if a store buys an item at a cost price (CP) of £250 and fixes the selling price (SP) at £300, then the actual profit (P) and profit rate or profit margin from the sale is calculated as follows:

$$\textbf{Sell price (SP) = £300} \qquad \textbf{Cost price (CP) = £250}$$

$$P = SP - CP$$
$$= £300 - £250$$
$$= £50$$

$$Rate = {}^{P}/_{CP} \times 100\%$$
$$= {}^{£50}/_{£250} \times 100\%$$
$$= 20\% \text{ profit}$$

VAT

VAT (Value Added Tax) is currently set at 17.5% in the UK and 21% in the Republic of Ireland. VAT applies to most transactions. Other countries call this tax different names; for example, Goods and Services Tax or Sales Tax.

 e.g.

If an item costs €65 without VAT, then the final cost is calculated as follows:

$$\textbf{Cost excluding VAT} = €65$$
$$\textbf{Cost including VAT} = €65 + (21\% \text{ of } €65)$$
$$= €65 + €13.65$$
$$= €78.65$$

Since adding VAT adds 21% of the original cost, the final cost is 121% of the original cost or 1.21 times the original cost – in this case 1.21 x €65 = €78.65. Thus, if the VAT is already included, the original cost is found through dividing the final cost by 1.21 – in this case €78.65 ÷ 1.21 = €65

Note: The '£' and '€' have been used alternately in these equations, for both UK and Irish users.

Data representation

Arrow diagram

Arrow diagrams have three main uses:

1. To show a relationship between the members of two sets.

   e.g.

   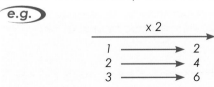

2. To link members of a set with other members according to specified criteria.

   e.g.

   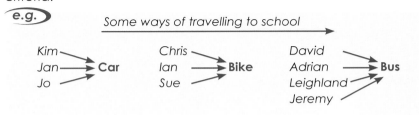

3. To solve problems involving combinations.

   e.g.

   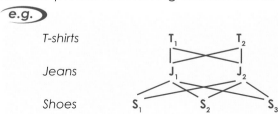

Carroll diagram

A grid-like structure for categorising results. The example below shows coloured blocks sorted into a 2 by 2 system.

e.g.

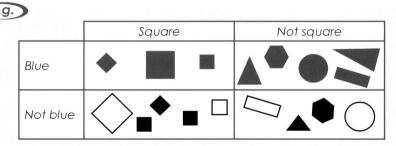

Venn diagram

A diagram that represents sets and their relationships. The example below shows the same coloured blocks as in the Carroll diagram sorted using a Venn diagram.

e.g.

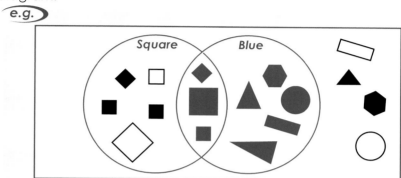

Tally marks

Marks used to record items, scores or events, and usually grouped in fives by a diagonal stroke. In the example below, the tally is used to record the heights, which are then collated into the table under the frequency column.

Table of data

A table is a means of organising data in rows and columns for a particular purpose. The example below shows the data for the heights of a class of pupils.

e.g.

Height in centimetres of 11-year-old pupils

Height in cm	Tally	Frequency
108	I	1
112	III	3
115	II	2
119	IIII	4
120	III	3
122	IIII	4
123	IHHI	6
126	II	2
130	I	1
132	III	3
137	I	1

Measures of central tendency

There are three common measures of central tendency for a set of data, such as heights of pupils.

Mode

From this table we can see that the modal or most commonly occurring height is 123 cm. [Note that sometimes there may be more than one mode; e.g. if there were only three pupils who were 123 cm tall, the heights of 119 cm and 122 cm would be the most commonly occurring ones, so the data would be bi-modal, or have two modes.]

Height in cm	Tally	Frequency
108	|	*1*
112	|||	*3*
115	||	*2*
119	||||	*4*
120	|||	*3*
122	||||	*4*
123	~~||||~~ |	*6*
126	||	*2*
130	|	*1*
132	|||	*3*
137	|	*1*

Median

The median (or middle) height may be found by locating the midpoint in the data when the data is arranged in order. Arranging the heights in order from shortest to tallest:

108, 112, 112, 112, 115, 115, 119, 119, 119, 119, 120, 120, 120, 122, 122, 122, 122, 123, 123, 123, 123, 123, 123, 126, 126, 130, 132, 132, 132, 137

So the median height is 122 cm, as there are 13 heights less and 13 heights more than 122.

If there were 29 pupils, the middle height or 15th height would be the median.

If there were only 28 pupils, the median would be between the 14th and 15th heights—thus the mean of the 14th and 15th heights.

Mean

The mean or average height is found by adding the heights of all the pupils and dividing by the number of pupils. In the above example, the total of all the heights added together is 3651, and this is divided by the number of pupils, 30; i.e. mean = 3651 cm ÷ 30 = 121.7 cm.

Bar chart (Bar graph; Column graph)

A visual way to represent a set of data by bars (rectangles) of equal width. The length of each bar/column corresponds to the size or frequency. Bars may be vertical or horizontal. Usually the bars or columns only touch each other if the data is continuous; and for discrete data, there is a space left between each bar or column.

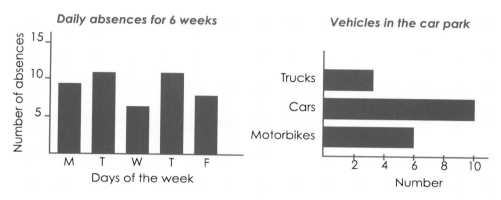

A bar chart may be used to represent more than one set of data. This is achieved by subdividing the bars to represent the components [known as a component, composite, stacked or sectional bar chart]; or the data can be displayed with bars alongside each other [known as a compound or multiple bar chart]. Examples are shown below.

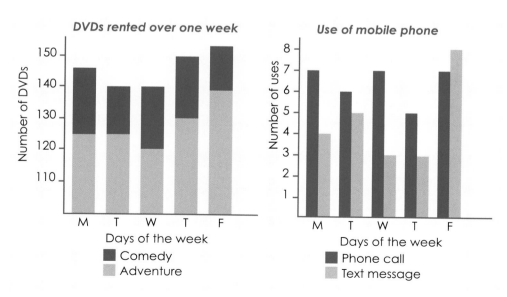

Data representation

Block graph

A type of chart or column graph where each bar or column is divided to show all individual pieces of data.

 e.g.

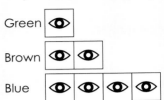

Eye colours in our group

Green

Brown

Blue

Box and whisker plot (Boxplot)

A graphical summary of data that shows five aspects of the data: the lower and upper quartiles (hence inter-quartile range), the median and the lowest and highest values.

e.g.

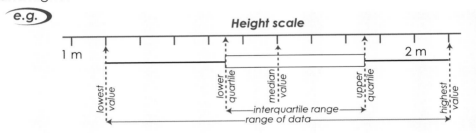

Height scale

1 m   2 m

lowest value

lower quartile

median value

upper quartile

highest value

—interquartile range—

—range of data—

Column chart/graph

[see Bar chart]

Cumulative frequency graph (Ogive)

A graph on which the cumulative frequencies are plotted and the points are joined, either by line segments (forming a cumulative frequency polygon) or, where there are sufficient points, a curve (sometimes referred to as a cumulative frequency curve, or ogive). To produce a cumulative frequency graph, data needs to be recorded on a table where the frequencies are successively totalled; e.g. the number of children couples have, as below.

 e.g.

Number of children	Number of couples (f)	Cumulative frequency (cf)
0	4	4
1	7	11
2	24	35
3	9	44
4	5	49
5	1	50

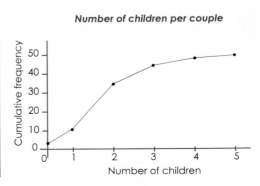

Number of children per couple

Histogram

A graph that looks like a vertical bar chart but has no space between successive bars. The height of each bar or column represents frequency. The frequencies are shown on the vertical axis and classes on the horizontal axis.The area of each bar may or may not be of equal width. There are no gaps between the bars, so when the width of each bar is the same, it appears like a bar chart.

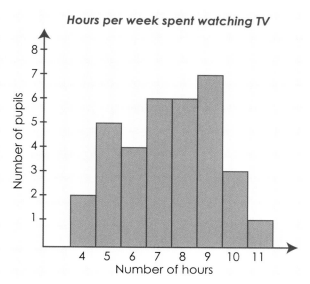

Hours per week spent watching TV

Some of the differences between a histogram and a bar chart

Histogram	Bar chart
Only used to show how frequently some quantity occurs.	May be used to show information other than frequency.
Does not have gaps between the columns.	May or may not have gaps between the columns.
Bars are vertical.	Bars may be horizontal or vertical.
The height of each column represents the frequency.	The length of each rectangle represents the frequency.
The arrangement of the columns is important as the horizontal axis represents values that have been counted or measured. The columns are placed so that the categories of data they represent are in numerical order.	The order of the columns is not generally important.
Categories of data with no actual data are shown on the scale.	Categories of data with no actual data are not necessarily shown on the scale.

Data representation

Frequency polygon

Also called a cumulative frequency polygon and formed by joining the midpoints of the tops of the bars of a histogram by line segments, which are connected at the start and finish of the graph to produce a polygon, with the area of the polygon being the same as the combined area of the bars, where the bars are of equal width.

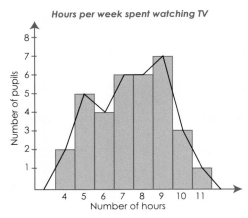

Hours per week spent watching TV

Line graph

Formed by line segments connecting points representing certain data, and with the horizontal axis usually indicating a measure of time; normally used for continuous or measurement data. Values can only be read accurately from the marked points, although estimates can be made from other positions along the line segments (interpolation); or beyond the points (extrapolation), which is more speculative. [See Cumulative frequency graph and Frequency polygon as special cases of line graphs.]

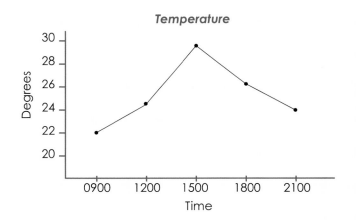

Temperature

Pictogram (Pictograph; Picture graph)

Data represented in picture form, where one picture may represent one or more units. When different pictures are used, they should be aligned on the chart.

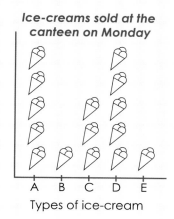

Ice-creams sold at the canteen on Monday

Types of ice-cream

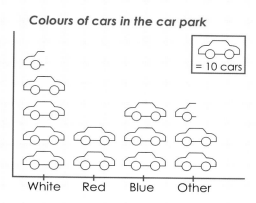

Colours of cars in the car park

= 10 cars

Pie chart (Pie graph; Circle graph)

The sectors of a circle are used to show a whole in terms of its parts.

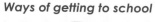

Ways of getting to school

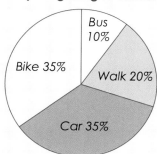

Bus 10%

Bike 35%

Walk 20%

Car 35%

Data representation

Scattergraph (Scattergram; Scatter plot)

A graph of plotted points which display the relationship between pairs of data sets. It uses bivariate data, which is information collected for the purpose of comparison. ['Bi' meaning two variables—most graphs referred to previously have been univariate—one variable.] Used to indicate the extent of any correlation between the pairs of data sets, which is determined by the spread pattern of the plots. Examples of some of the types of results are shown below.

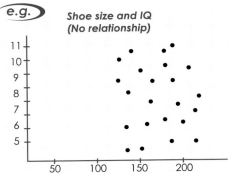

e.g.

Shoe size and IQ
(No relationship)

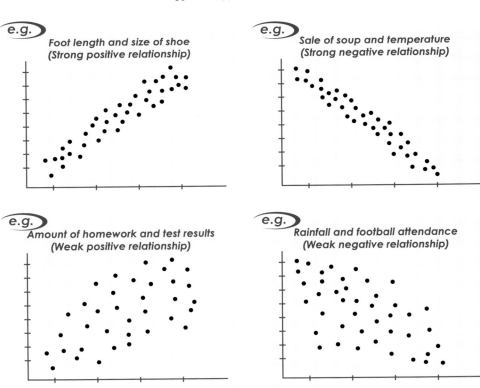

e.g.

Foot length and size of shoe
(Strong positive relationship)

e.g.

Sale of soup and temperature
(Strong negative relationship)

e.g.

Amount of homework and test results
(Weak positive relationship)

e.g.

Rainfall and football attendance
(Weak negative relationship)

Stem and leaf plot

Display of data with its frequency, using part of the value of the data on one side of the plot (the stem); and the remainder of the value on the other side of the plot (the leaf).

Scores in a game

Stem	Leaves
1	9 6 9
2	1 7 6 4 8
3	4 5 2

So the scores were: 19, 16, 19, 21, 27, 26, 24, 28, 34, 35 and 32

Comparison of male and female pulse rates

Females		Males
0	10	
2 8	9	2
4 6 5 8 1	8	6 3 5
5 0 7 6	7	3 5 4 2 3 4
3 5 8 1 3	6	0 7 8 5
5	5	2 9

Reading from the top the female pulse rates were 100, 92, 98, 84, 86 etc. The male pulse rates were 92, 86, 83, 85, 73 etc.

Tree diagram

A diagram beginning with one operation that branches out to represent the possible outcomes, with the process repeated at each branch for each successive operation. The example below shows the possible results of three successive coin tosses.

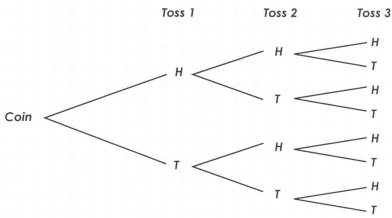

Angles and parallels

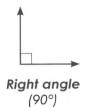

Right angle
(90°)

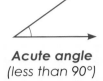

Acute angle
(less than 90°)

Obtuse angle
(greater than 90° and less than 180°)

Straight angle
(180°)

Reflex angle
(greater than 180° and less than 360°)

One rotation
(360°)

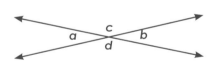

Vertically opposite angles
Angle pairs a & b, and c & d are
vertically opposite and congruent.

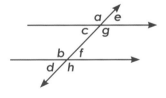

Corresponding angles
Pairs a & b, c & d, e & f, g & h are
corresponding, congruent angles.

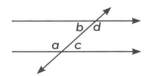

Co-interior angles
Angle pairs a & b, and c & d are
co-interior and are supplementary;
i.e. each pair adds up to 180°.

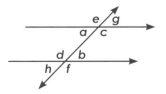

Alternate angles
Pairs a & b, c & d, e & f, g & h are
alternate, congruent angles.

A polygon is any simple closed curve consisting only of line segments; e.g. triangles and quadrilaterals are the most common polygons. [From the Greek *polus* meaning 'many' and *gonia* meaning 'angle'.] Examples of the first 10 polygons including each regular form [all sides congruent; all angles congruent], are shown in the table below.

Name	Sides	Irregular	Regular
Triangle	3		
Quadrilateral	4		
Pentagon	5		
Hexagon	6		
Heptagon (Septagon)	7		
Octagon	8		
Nonagon	9		
Decagon	10		
Unidecagon (Undecagon)	11		
Dodecagon (Duodecagon)	12		

Triangles

Classifying triangles

All triangles may be classified according to their sides or according to their angles as follows.

By sides	**By angles**

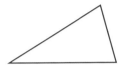

Scalene triangle
No sides or angles congruent.

Acute-angled triangle
All angles are acute.

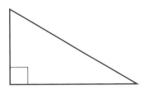

Isosceles triangle
Two sides congruent and the angles opposite them are also congruent.

Right-angled triangle
One of the angles is a right angle.

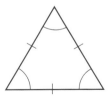

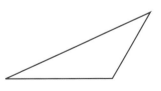

Equilateral triangle
All three sides congruent and the angles opposite them are also congruent (60° each).

Obtuse-angled triangle
One of the angles is an obtuse angle.

The Complete Handbook of Maths Terms   www.prim-ed.com   Prim-Ed Publishing

Triangles may also be classified by combining sizes of angles and sides.

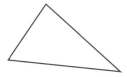

Acute scalene triangle
All angles less than 90° and no sides the same length.

Acute isosceles triangle
All angles less than 90° and two sides the same length.

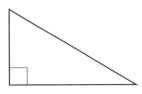

Right scalene triangle
One right angle and no sides the same length.

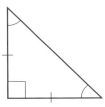

Right isosceles triangle
One right angle and two sides the same length.

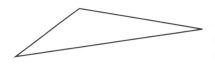

Obtuse scalene triangle
One angle greater than 90° and no sides the same length.

Obtuse isosceles triangle
One angle greater than 90° and two sides the same length.

Triangles

Other triangle facts

Sum of the angles in a triangle   *e.g.*

The sum of the angles in a triangle is always 180°.

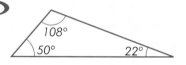

Exterior angles   *e.g.*

Each exterior angle is equal to the sum of the two opposite interior angles.

Pythagorean theorem   *e.g.*

In a right-angled triangle the square on the hypotenuse is equal to the sum of the squares on the other two sides [see p. 43].

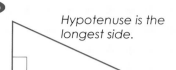

Hypotenuse is the longest side.

Similar triangles

Two triangles are similar if they have the same shape, but not necessarily the same size. Being the same shape means that corresponding angles are congruent and the corresponding sides are in the same ratio [see below].

Conditions for similarity	Diagram
Side-side-side (SSS) *If the lengths of the three corresponding sides (SSS) of two triangles are in the same ratio, then the triangles are similar.*	
Angle-angle (AA) *If two angles of a triangle are congruent to two angles of another triangle, then the triangles are similar.*	
Side-angle-side (SAS) *If one angle of a triangle is congruent to one angle of another triangle and the lengths of the sides (SAS) that determine these angles are in the same ratio, then the triangles are similar. [Note that the angles that are congruent must be between the sides that are in the same ratio, hence the A is placed in the centre of the SAS as a reminder.]*	

Congruent triangles

Two triangles are congruent if they are exactly the same size and shape. Certain conditions need to be met for two triangles to be congruent, as shown below.

Conditions for congruency	Diagram
Side-side-side (SSS) *If three sides of one triangle are congruent to three sides of another triangle then the triangles are congruent.*	
Side-angle-side (SAS) *If two sides and the included angle of one triangle are the same as two sides and the included angle of another triangle then the triangles are congruent.*	
Angle-angle-side (AAS) *If two angles and any side of one triangle are congruent to two angles and the corresponding side of another triangle then the triangles are congruent.*	
Right angle-hypotenuse-side (RHS) *If the hypotenuse and another side of one right triangle are congruent to the corresponding hypotenuse and side of the other right triangle, then the triangles are congruent.*	

Trigonometric ratios

In trigonometry the sides of a right triangle are given special names. In the triangle ABC, when using angle A as a reference point, AB is referred to as the adjacent side, BC as the opposite side and AC as the hypotenuse. However, if angle C is the reference point then BC is the adjacent side, AB the opposite side, and AC still remains the hypotenuse [as it is opposite the right angle and it is always the longest side].

The following trigonometric ratios are related to angle A.

The sine (sin) of angle A is calculated by the ratio:

$$sin = \frac{opposite}{hypotenuse} = \frac{BC}{AC}$$

The cosine (cos) of angle A is calculated by the ratio:

$$cos = \frac{adjacent}{hypotenuse} = \frac{AB}{AC}$$

The tangent (tan) of angle A is calculated by the ratio:

$$tan = \frac{opposite}{adjacent} = \frac{BC}{AB}$$

Quadrilaterals

Quadrilaterals are the most common type of polygon in our environment. The different types of quadrilaterals are explained and illustrated in the table below.

Definition	Diagram
Quadrilateral Any polygon that has four sides [Latin *quadri*, four, and *latus*, side.]	
Trapezium (Trapezoid) A quadrilateral with only one pair of parallel sides. [Note: Some mathematics texts define a trapezium as a quadrilateral with *at least* one pair of parallel sides.]	
Isosceles trapezium (Isosceles trapezoid) A trapezium in which the non-parallel sides are congruent. [Note: Thus it is symmetrical.]	
Parallelogram A quadrilateral with both pairs of opposite sides parallel. Properties Sides: Opposite sides are congruent. Angles: Opposite angles are congruent; co-interior angles are supplementary. Diagonals: Triangles formed by each diagonal are congruent; diagonals bisect each other.	
Rhombus A parallelogram with four sides congruent. Properties A rhombus has all the properties of a parallelogram and the following: Diagonals: Its diagonals bisect each other at right angles, and also bisect the angles of the rhombus.	

Definition	Diagram
Rectangle A parallelogram with all angles right angles. Properties A rectangle has all the properties of a parallelogram and the following: Diagonals: Its diagonals are the same length.	
Square A special rectangle and a special rhombus with all sides and all angles congruent. Properties A square has all the properties of a parallelogram/rhombus/rectangle.	
Oblong A rectangle that is not square. Properties [See Rectangle above.]	
Kite A symmetrical quadrilateral with two shorter congruent sides and two longer congruent sides. Properties Diagonals: Its diagonals are perpendicular, and the shorter one is bisected.	
Arrowhead (Chevron, Dart, Delta) A concave quadrilateral with two pairs of congruent adjacent sides. [Can be considered as a concave kite.]	

Circles

A circle is the set of all points in a plane that are the same distance from a centre point. All circles have the same properties; they only vary in size. The components and properties are shown in the table below.

Definition	Diagram
Circumference The perimeter or distance around the outside of the circle [the length of the circle].	
Diameter A line segment from one 'side' of the circle through its centre to the other 'side' of the circle, as shown. [The longest chord of a circle.]	
Radius A line segment from the centre of the circle to the circle itself, as shown. [Any diameter consists of two radii.]	
Chord A line segment joining two points of the circumference of a circle. The diameter is a chord that passes through the centre of the circle.	
Major/Minor arc A part of the circumference of the circle. If the part represents more than half of the circumference, then it is referred to as a major arc; if less, then it is referred to as a minor arc.	
Major/Minor segment The part of the circular region enclosed between a chord (not a diameter) and the circle is called a segment. If the segment covers a region greater than that of the semicircle, it is called a major segment (see shaded section); if smaller, then a minor segment (see unshaded section).	

Definition	Diagram
Quadrant One fourth (quarter) of a circular region, formed when two radii are at right angles to each other.	
Semicircle Half a circular region, formed by the diameter and half the circle.	
Concentric circles Two or more circles that share the same centre.	
Annulus The plane region between two concentric circles	*annulus*
Tangent A line that intersects the circle at one point. [A tangent is always perpendicular to the radius at the point of intersection.]	*tangent*
Sector Portion of a circular region bounded by two radii and an arc. If the sector covers a region greater than that of the semicircle, it is called a major sector (see shaded section); if smaller, then it is called a minor sector (see unshaded section).	*minor sector* *major sector*

Circles

Circle angle properties

Angles in a segment	**Angles in a semicircle**	**Cyclic quadrilateral**
All angles in the same segment are congruent.	All angles in a semicircle are right angles.	Opposite angles of a cyclic quadrilateral add up to 180°; a + c = 180°; b + d = 180°.

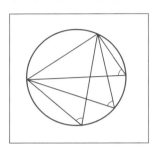 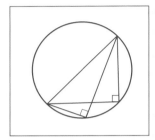 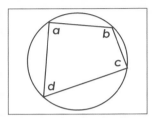

Circle-related formulas

Circumference

The circumference (C) of a circle may be calculated by multiplying the diameter (D) of a circle by the ratio pi (approx 3.1416) as follows:

$C = \pi \times D$

Alternatively, the diameter is twice the radius (D = 2r) so the circumference may be calculated as follows:

$C = \pi \times 2r = 2\pi r$

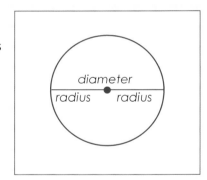

Area of a circular region

The area (A) of any circular region can be found as follows, using its radius (r) and the pi ratio.

$A = \pi r^2$

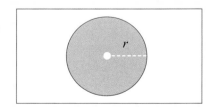

Polyhedra

Polyhedra are three-dimensional (3-D) shapes consisting of plane faces (the singular term is polyhedron). They are solid shapes that have length, width and height. The polyhedron shown here is a hexahedron; i.e. it has six faces.

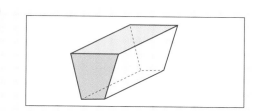

There are five regular polyhedra, known as the Platonic solids [see p. 99].

Prisms

Three-dimensional shapes with parallel and congruent end faces, with the shape of the pair of congruent faces giving each prism its name. Below are some examples of prisms.

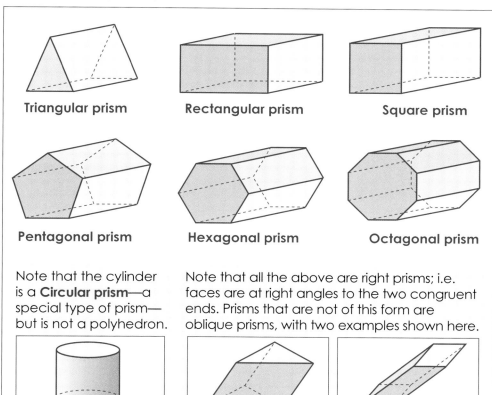

Triangular prism   Rectangular prism   Square prism

Pentagonal prism   Hexagonal prism   Octagonal prism

Note that the cylinder is a **Circular prism**—a special type of prism—but is not a polyhedron.

Note that all the above are right prisms; i.e. faces are at right angles to the two congruent ends. Prisms that are not of this form are oblique prisms, with two examples shown here.

Three-dimensional shapes

Pyramids

A pyramid is a polyhedron with a polygonal base and the other faces are triangles with a common vertex. Below are some examples of pyramids.

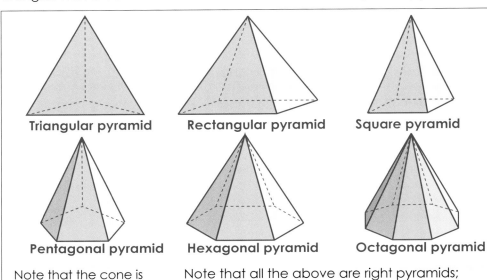

Triangular pyramid   **Rectangular pyramid**   **Square pyramid**

Pentagonal pyramid   **Hexagonal pyramid**   **Octagonal pyramid**

Note that the cone is a **Circular pyramid**—a special type of pyramid—but is not a polyhedron.

Note that all the above are right pyramids; i.e. the apex is above the centre of the base. Pyramids that are not of this form are oblique pyramids, with two examples shown here.

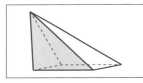

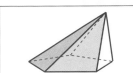

Spheres and ovoids

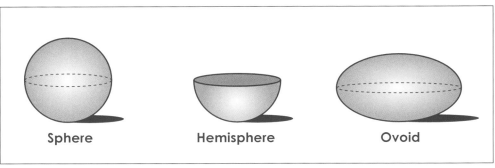

Sphere   **Hemisphere**   **Ovoid**

Platonic solids

The Platonic solids [see p. 40] consist of five polyhedra in which all faces are congruent and all angles are congruent. There are only five such regular solids, and these are illustrated below, together with examples of 2-D nets that fold up to make the 3-D shapes. The 4 faces of the tetrahedron, 8 faces of the octahedron, and 20 faces of the icosahedron are all equilateral triangles. The 6 faces of the hexahedron (cube) are all regular quadrilaterals (squares), while the 12 faces of the dodecahedron are regular pentagons.

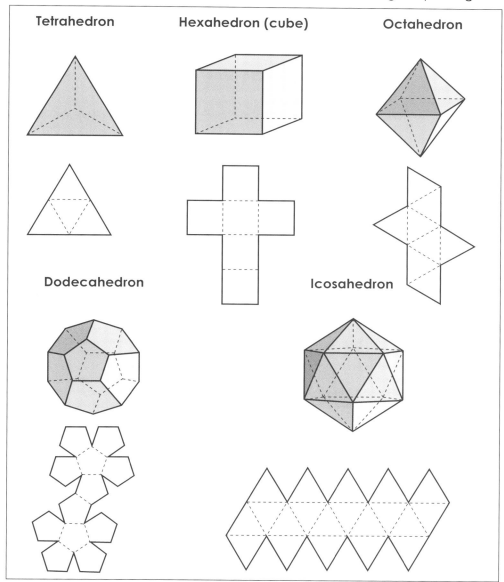

Tetrahedron   Hexahedron (cube)   Octahedron

Dodecahedron   Icosahedron

Euler's law

In all polyhedra, there is a relationship between the numbers of vertices or corners (V), faces (F) and edges (E). This can be expressed as $V + F = E + 2$.

For example, in the square pyramid to the right, there are 5 vertices, 5 faces and 8 edges, so the relationship is seen as $5 + 5 = 8 + 2$.

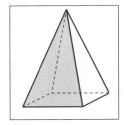

Euler's Law applies to all pyramids and prisms, and thus to the two special cases that are not polyhedra; i.e. the circular pyramid (cone) and the circular prism (cylinder), as shown below. [The curved surfaces are not faces.]

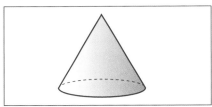

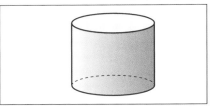

Cone
$V = 1$
$F = 1$
$E = 0$

$V + F = E + 2$
$1 + 1 = 0 + 2$

Cylinder
$V = 0$
$F = 2$
$E = 0$

$V + F = E + 2$
$0 + 2 = 0 + 2$

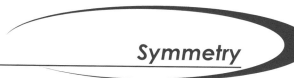
Reflectional symmetry

This is the correspondence, in size, form and arrangement, of parts of an object or figure on opposite sides of a point, line, axis or plane.

2-D: Lines of symmetry
One line of symmetry

More than one line of symmetry

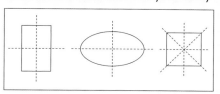

Asymmetry
No lines of symmetry

3-D: Planes of symmetry
The diagram below shows one of the planes of symmetry of a cube, which has a total of nine planes of symmetry.

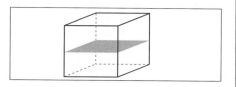

Rotational symmetry

An object or figure has rotational symmetry if it appears to retain its original orientation after rotating through some fraction of a complete turn about a fixed point.

This shape has an order of rotation of 4, as in one full 360° rotation, there are 4 places where it looks the same as the original.

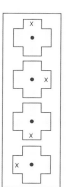

This shape has an order of rotation of 3, as in one full 360° rotation, there are 3 places where it looks the same as the original.

Note: If a shape can only be rotated once to return to its original position, it does not have rotational symmetry. There is no order of rotation of 1. For example, the triangle below does not have rotational symmetry.

3-D: Axes of symmetry
The diagram below shows one of the axes of symmetry of a tetrahedron. It has an order of rotational symmetry of three about the axis shown.

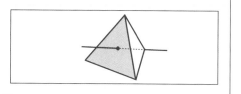

Transformations

A transformation is the process by which an object or figure is changed in shape, size or position.

Euclidean or congruent transformations

Translations, reflections and rotations are all Euclidean translations. In these translations the length, width, angle size and area do not change. Thus, both the original object or figure and its translated form (image) are congruent, as shown below.

Translation (Slide)

A translation is the process by which an object or figure changes position, without turning, for a given distance in a given direction.

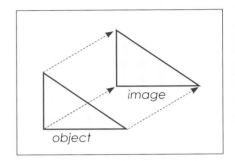

Reflection (Flip)

A reflection is the mirror image of an object or figure, where each point of the object is the same distance from the 'mirror line' as its corresponding point on the image.

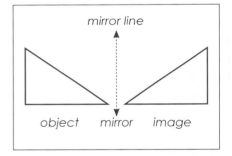

Rotation (Turn)

A rotation is the process by which an object or figure changes position by rotating about a fixed point through a given angle.

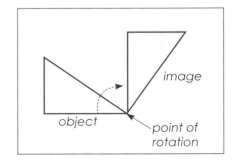

Non-Euclidean or similarity transformations (Dilations)

The increase or decrease in the size of an object or figure is a non-Euclidean transformation. The resulting image is the same shape as the original (similar).

Enlargement

An enlargement is an increase in the size of an object or figure while maintaining the same shape.

Point projection

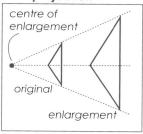

Enlargement by grid

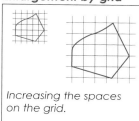

Increasing the spaces on the grid.

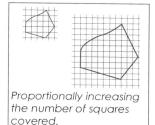

Proportionally increasing the number of squares covered.

Reduction

A reduction is a decrease in the size of an object or figure while maintaining the same shape.

Point projection

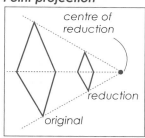

Reduction by grid

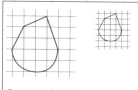

Decreasing the spaces on the grid.

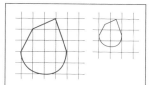

Proportionally decreasing the number of squares covered.

Distortion transformations

A distortion transformation is the process of changing both the shape and size of an object or figure so that its image is still topologically the same.

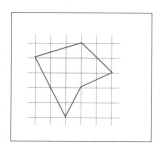

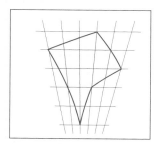

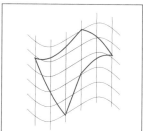

Cross-sections and conic sections

Cross-sections refer to the plane regions resulting from planar cuts through 3-D objects.

Some cross-sections of cubes

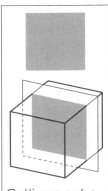

Cutting a cube horizontally or vertically parallel to any face produces a square cross-section.

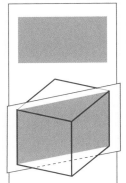

Cutting a cube from one edge to another produces a rectangular cross-section.

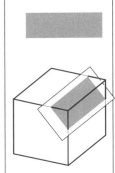

Cutting an edge off a cube produces a rectangular cross-section.

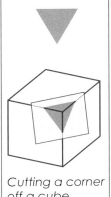

Cutting a corner off a cube produces a triangular cross-section.

There are many other resulting cross sections of a cube, such as trapeziums and hexagons.

Some cross-sections of cylinders

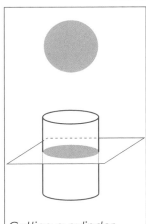

Cutting a cylinder horizontally produces a circular cross-section.

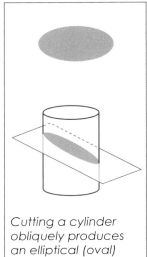

Cutting a cylinder obliquely produces an elliptical (oval) cross-section.

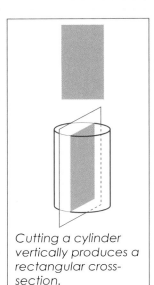

Cutting a cylinder vertically produces a rectangular cross-section.

The Complete Handbook of Maths Terms   www.prim-ed.com   Prim-Ed Publishing

Cross-sections and conic sections

Cross-sections of cones (conic sections)

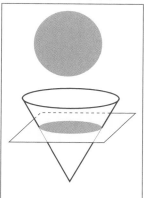

Cutting a cone horizontally produces a circular cross-section.

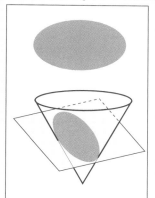

Cutting a cone obliquely produces an elliptical (oval) cross-section.

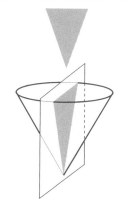

Cutting a cone vertically through the centre produces an isosceles triangular cross-section.

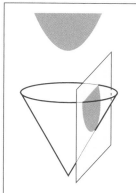

Cutting a cone vertically but not through the centre produces half a hyperbola cross-section.

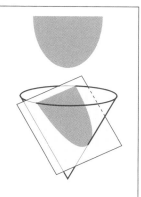

Cutting a cone diagonally and parallel to its slope produces a parabola cross-section.

The International System (SI)

There are three kinds of SI units:
1. Base units
2. Supplementary units
3. Derived units—Complex names and Special names

SI base units

Physical quantity	Unit	Symbol
Length	metre	m
Mass	kilogram	kg
Time	second	s
Electric current	ampere	A
Thermodynamic temperature	kelvin	K
Luminous intensity	candela	cd
Amount of substance	mole	mol

SI supplementary units

Physical quantity	Unit	Symbol
Plane angle	radian	rad
Solid angle	steradian	sr

Examples of derived units—Complex names

Physical quantity	Unit	Symbol
Area	square metre	m^2
Volume	cubic metre	m^3
Density	kilogram per cubic metre	kg/m^3
Speed	metre per second	m/s

Examples of derived units—Special names

Physical quantity	Unit	Symbol
Force	newton	N
Pressure	pascal	Pa
Work/Energy/Heat	joule	J
Power	watt	W

The International System (SI)

In SI there is only one unit name for each physical quantity, with multiples and sub-multiples of the unit recorded by using prefixes.

SI prefixes and names

Prefix	Symbol	Power	Name	Numeral
tera	T	10^{12}	trillion	1 000 000 000 000
giga	G	10^9	billion	1 000 000 000
mega	M	10^6	million	1 000 000
kilo	k	10^3	thousand	1 000
hecto	h	10^2	hundred	100
deka	da	10^1	ten	10
deci	d	10^{-1}	tenth	0.1
centi	c	10^{-2}	hundredth	0.01
milli	m	10^{-3}	thousandth	0.001
micro	μ	10^{-6}	millionth	0.000 001
nano	n	10^{-9}	billionth	0.000 000 001
pico	p	10^{-12}	trillionth	0.000 000 000 001

SI does not use all the metric system prefixes but only the base units in multiples of thousands and thousandths. For example the most common SI length units used are the metre (base unit, m), a thousandth of a metre (millimetre, mm), and a thousand times a metre (kilometre, km). Thus h, da, d, c are not generally used internationally, but some of these prefixes are in wide use in many countries. For example, the centimetre (cm) is used for school, household and clothing measurements. Below are the common equivalents and approximate factors for some mental conversions.

Length

10 millimetres (mm) = 1 centimetre (cm)
1000 millimetres   = 1 metre (m)
100 centimetres   = 1 metre
1000 metres   = 1 kilometre (km)

Approximate Metric/Imperial equivalent lengths

25 mm   ≈ 1 inch
2.5 cm   ≈ 1 inch
(so 1 cm ≈ 0.4 inch)
30 cm   ≈ 1 foot
91 cm   ≈ 1 yard
1.6 km   ≈ 1 mile
(so 1 km ≈ 0.6 mile)

The International System (SI)

Area

100 square millimetres (mm^2)	= 1 square centimetre (cm^2)
10 000 square centimetres	= 1 square metre (m^2)
1 000 000 square metres	= 1 square kilometre (km^2)
10 000 square metres	= 1 hectare (ha)
100 hectares	= 1 square kilometre

Approximate Metric/ Imperial equivalent areas

1 ha ≈ 2.5 acres
(so 1 acre ≈ 0.4 ha)
1 km^2 ≈ 0.4 square miles
(so 1 square mile ≈ 2.5 km^2)

Volume

1000 cubic millimetres (mm^3)	= 1 cubic centimetre (cm^3)
1000 cubic centimetres	= 1 cubic decimetre (dm^3)
1 000 000 cubic centimetres	= 1 cubic metre (m^3)

Approximate Metric/ Imperial equivalent volumes

1 m^3 ≈ 1.3 cubic yards
(so 1 cubic yard ≈ 0.75 m^3)

Capacity

1000 millilitres (mL)	= 1 litre (L)
1000 litres	= 1 kilolitre (kL)

Approximate Metric/Imperial equivalent capacities

1 L ≈ 0.22 gallons
(so 1 gallon ≈ 4.5 L)

Mass

1000 grams (g)	= 1 kilogram (kg)
1000 kilograms	= 1 tonne (t)

Approximate Metric/Imperial equivalent masses

1 kg ≈ 2.2 pounds
(so 1 pound ≈ 0.45 kg)
1t ≈ 1 ton

Speed

1 kilometre per hour (km/h) ≈ 0.28 metres per second (m/s)

Temperature

The degree Celsius (°C) rather than the kelvin is used for everyday situations. On the Celsius scale the freezing point of pure water at sea level is 0 °C and the boiling point is 100 °C.
Note that:

$$0 \ °C = 32° \ Fahrenheit$$
$$100 \ °C = 212° \ Fahrenheit$$
$$°C = \frac{5}{9}(°F - 32°)$$
$$°F = \frac{9}{5}°C + 32°$$

The Mass/Volume/Capacity link

1. One cubic centimetre of water is one millilitre and has a mass of one gram; i.e. 1 cm^3 = 1 mL = 1 g of water.

2. One cubic decimetre of water is one litre and has a mass of one kilogram; i.e. 1 dm^3 = 1 L = 1 kg of water.

3. One cubic metre of water is one kilolitre and has a mass of one tonne; i.e. 1 m^3 = 1 kL = 1 t of water.

All countries also use non-SI units, especially those for time and angular measure, and in both these cases there is a link to the ancient Babylonians who used a base of 60 in their numeration system.

Time

$$
\begin{aligned}
60 \text{ seconds (s)} &= 1 \text{ minute (min)} \\
60 \text{ minutes} &= 1 \text{ hour (h)} \\
24 \text{ hours} &= 1 \text{ day} \\
7 \text{ days} &= 1 \text{ week} \\
2 \text{ weeks} &= 1 \text{ fortnight} \\
52 \text{ weeks } 1 \text{ day} &= 1 \text{ year} \\
52 \text{ weeks } 2 \text{ days} &= 1 \text{ leap year} \\
365 \text{ days} &= 1 \text{ year} \\
366 \text{ days} &= 1 \text{ leap year} \\
12 \text{ months} &= 1 \text{ year} \\
10 \text{ years} &= 1 \text{ decade} \\
100 \text{ years} &= 1 \text{ century} \\
1000 \text{ years} &= 1 \text{ millennium}
\end{aligned}
$$

Days in each month

The verses below can be used to recall the days in each month.

Thirty days have September,
April, June and November.
February has twenty-eight;
And thirty-one the others date.
But if a leap year to assign,
Then February twenty-nine.

Thirty days hath September,
April, June and November.
All the rest have thirty-one;
Excepting February alone,
Which has twenty-eight days clear,
And twenty-nine in each leap year.

By clenching both fists alongside each other, the days in all the months can also be recalled by checking the knuckles and the gaps as shown in the diagram.

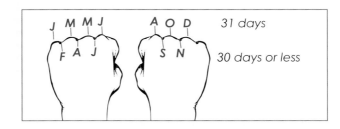

Non-SI units

Months of the year

January .... 31 days		July .... 31 days	
February .... 28 or 29 days		August .... 31 days	
March .... 31 days		September ..... 30 days	
April .... 30 days		October .... 31 days	
May .... 31 days		November ..... 30 days	
June .... 30 days		December ..... 31 days	

Years and leap years

The length of a solar year is almost 365 $^1/_4$ days (actually 365 days, 5 hours, 48 minutes, 45 seconds) as this is the time it takes the Earth to complete its orbit around the Sun. Thus, each four years it is necessary to add one day, so that while a year has 365 days, a leap year has 366 days. 1980, 1984, 1988, 1992, 1996, and 2004 were all leap years because each number is divisible by four. However, to correct for the fact that a day added every four years is slightly too much, century years are only leap years if divisible by 400. Thus 1600 and 2000 were both leap years, but 1700, 1800 and 1900 were not leap years. [This slight change was made by Pope Gregory in 1582, so the calendar in universal use is called the Gregorian Calendar, although it was originally developed by Julius Caesar, with a slight change made by Caesar Augustus—thus the months of Julius (July) and Augustus (August). The old Roman calendar had 10 months and we still use the Latin prefixes for 7, 8, 9 and 10 in the names for September, October, November and December.]

24-hour time

Time can be expressed in 12-hour (am/pm) format or in 24-hour format. Note that when writing 24-hour time, neither punctuation nor spaces are used; e.g. 0638 = 6.38 am; 1245 = 12.45 pm; 2217 = 10.17 pm. The graphic table below can be used to convert from one format to another.

International standard date notation

This format is YYYY-MM-DD where YYYY is the year, MM is the month and DD is the day of the month. Thus 2006-09-03 (or 20060903) represents 3 September 2006.

Angular measure

$$
\begin{aligned}
60 \text{ seconds} &= 1 \text{ minute} \\
60 \text{ minutes} &= 1 \text{ degree} \\
90 \text{ degrees} &= 1 \text{ right angle} \\
180 \text{ degrees} &= 1 \text{ straight angle} \\
360 \text{ degrees} &= 1 \text{ rotation} \\
57 \text{ degrees} &\approx 1 \text{ radian}
\end{aligned}
$$

Distance & speed

The nautical mile will continue to be used for navigational purposes because it is the length of an arc on the Earth's surface formed by an angle of one minute ($\frac{1}{60}°$) at the Earth's centre [see diagram below]. The knot is a unit of speed of one nautical mile per hour, and is usually applied to wind and boat speeds.

1 nautical mile ≈ 1.85 kilometres
1 nautical mile ≈ 1.16 Imperial miles
1 knot (kn) = 1 nautical mile per hour
1 kn ≈ 1.85 km/h

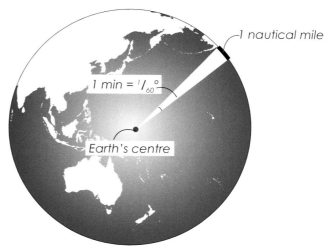

1 nautical mile

$1 \text{ min} = \frac{1}{60}°$

Earth's centre

Note: Not drawn to scale.

Thus, the circumference of the Earth = 360° x 60 nautical miles
= 21 600 nautical miles

Metric ⟷ imperial conversion table

The conversion factors listed below are shown to four significant figures and are more precise than those given on the preceding pages. Use a calculator to work particular examples, following these methods:

1. To convert from imperial measures to SI or metric measures, **multiply** by the conversion factor.

2. To convert from SI or metric measures to imperial measures, **divide** by the conversion factor.

Quantity	Imperial	Conversion factor	Metric
Length	inches	25.40	millimetres
	inches	2.540	centimetres
	feet	0.3048	metres
	yards	0.9144	metres
	chains	20.12	metres
	miles	1.609	kilometres
Area	square inches	645.2	square millimetres
	square inches	6.452	square centimetres
	square feet	0.0929	square metres
	square yards	0.8361	square metres
	acres	0.4047	hectares
	square miles	2.590	square kilometres
Volume	cubic inches	16 390	cubic millimetres
	cubic inches	16.39	cubic centimetres
	cubic feet	0.0283	cubic metres
	cubic yards	0.7646	cubic metres
Capacity	fluid ounces	28.41	millilitres
	pints	0.5683	litres
	gallons	4.546	litres
Mass	ounces	28.35	grams
	pounds	0.4536	kilograms
	hundredweight	50.80	kilograms
	tons	1.016	tonnes
Speed	feet/second	0.3048	metres/second
	feet/minute	0.005080	metres/second
	miles/hour	1.609	kilometres/hour
	miles/hour	0.4470	metres/second

The Complete Handbook of Maths Terms   www.prim-ed.com   Prim-Ed Publishing

Square region
Area = length x length
$$A = l^2$$

l

l

Rectangular region
Area = length x width (or base x height)
$$A = lw \text{ (or } bh)$$

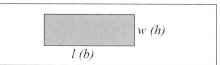

w (h)

l (b)

Parallelogram and rhombus region
Area = base x height
$$A = bh$$

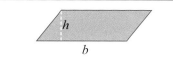

h

b

Trapezium region
Area $= \frac{1}{2}$ x sum of parallel sides x height
$$= \frac{1}{2}(a + b) \times h$$
$$A = \frac{1}{2}(a + b)h$$

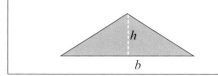

a

h

b

Triangular region
Area $= \frac{1}{2}$ x base x height
$$A = \frac{1}{2}bh$$

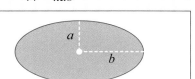

h

b

Circular region
Area = Pi x radius x radius
$$A = \pi r^2$$

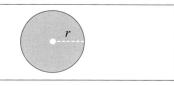

r

Elliptical (Oval) region
Area = Pi x a x b
$$A = \pi ab$$

a

b

Surface of a sphere
Area = 4 x Pi x radius x radius
$$A = 4\pi r^2$$

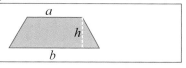

r

Surface of a cylinder
Area = (2 x area of base) + (Circ. x height)
$$= 2\pi r^2 + 2\pi rh$$
$$A = 2\pi r(r + h)$$

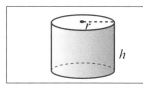

r

h

Surface of a cube
Area = 6 x Area of one face
$$A = 6l^2$$

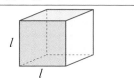

l

l

Rectangular prism (cuboid)

Volume = length x width(breadth) x height
$$= l \times w \times h$$
$$V = lwh \text{ (or } lbh)$$

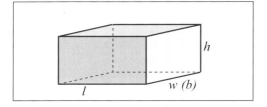

Cube

Volume = length x width(breadth) x height
$$= l \times l \times l$$
$$V = l^3$$

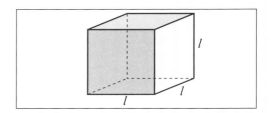

Triangular prism

Volume = Area of end region x length
$$= {}^{1}/_{2} \times \text{base} \times \text{height} \times \text{length}$$
$$= {}^{1}/_{2} \times b \times h \times l$$
$$V = {}^{1}/_{2} bhl$$

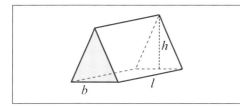

Trapezial prism

Volume = Area of end region x length
$$= {}^{1}/_{2} \times \text{sum of parallel sides} \times \text{height} \times \text{length}$$
$$= {}^{1}/_{2} (a + b) \times h \times l$$
$$V = {}^{1}/_{2} (a + b)hl$$

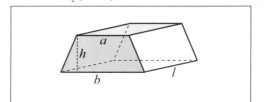

Circular prism (Cylinder)

Volume = Area of end region x length
$$= \pi r^2 \times l$$
$$V = \pi r^2 l$$

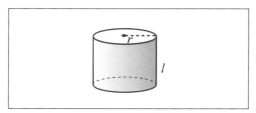

All prisms
Volume = Area of end region x length (or area of base x height)

Rectangular pyramid

Volume $= \frac{1}{3}$ x area of base x height

$\qquad = \frac{1}{3}$ x l x w x h

$\quad V = \frac{1}{3}lwh$

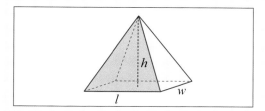

Square pyramid

Volume $= \frac{1}{3}$ x area of base x height

$\qquad = \frac{1}{3}$ x l x l x h

$\quad V = \frac{1}{3}l^2h$

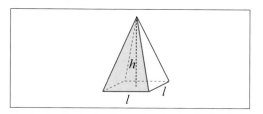

Triangular pyramid

Volume $= \frac{1}{3}$ x area of base x height

$\qquad = \frac{1}{3}$ x $\frac{1}{2}l$ x w x h

$\quad V = \frac{1}{6}lwh$

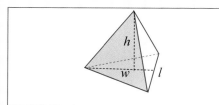

Circular pyramid (Cone)

Volume $= \frac{1}{3}$ x area of base x height

$\qquad = \frac{1}{3}$ x πr^2 x h

$\quad V = \frac{1}{3}\pi r^2h$

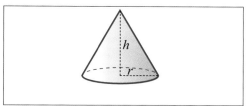

All pyramids

Volume $= \frac{1}{3}$ the volume of a prism with the same base and height

Sphere

Volume $= \frac{1}{3}$ x $4\pi r^3$

$\quad V = \frac{4}{3}\pi r^3$

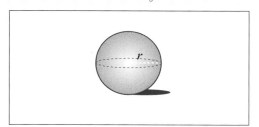

Common maths symbols

Symbol	Meaning
=	equals, is equal to, is the same as, is
≠	is not equal to
≈	is approximately equal to
>	is greater than
≥	is greater than or equal to
<	is less than
≤	is less than or equal to
≅	is congruent to
$a : b$	ratio of a to b or $^a/_b$
π	pi, approx 3.14 or 3.1416 or $^{22}/_7$
%	percent
$\sqrt{}$	the square root of
$\sqrt[3]{}$	the cube root of
$0.\overline{3}$	0.33333 … ; i.e. 0.3 recurring
!	factorial; e.g. 3! = 3 x 2 x 1
∞	infinity
°	degree
Δ	triangle; e.g. ΔABC means triangle ABC
∠	angle; e.g. ∠ABC means angle ABC
⊥	is perpendicular to
∟	a right angle